Earth, Energy and Environment

Timely Reports to Keep
Journalists, Scholars and the Public
Abreast of Developing Issues, Events and Trends

54843

Published by Congressional Quarterly, Inc.

1414 22nd Street N.W.
Washington, D.C. 20037

About the Cover

The cover was designed by Art Director Howard Chapman who, assisted by staff artist Richard Pottern, provided many of the graphics in this book.

PRINTED IN THE UNITED STATES OF AMERICA, JANUARY 1977

Editor, Hoyt Gimlin
Editorial Assistant, Lynda McNeil
Production Manager, I.D. Fuller
Assistant Production Manager, Kathleen E. Walsh

Library of Congress Cataloging in Publication Data

Congressional Quarterly Inc.
Editorial research reports on earth, energy, and environment.

Includes index.

1. Environmental policy—United States—Addresses, essays, lectures. 2. Energy policy—United States—Addresses, essays, lectures. I. Title. II. Title: Earth, energy and environment.
HC110.E5C667 1976   301.31'0973 76-57672
ISBN 0-87187-107-6

Contents

Contents

Foreword

The 1970s began as the "ecology decade"—the time when America's rising awareness of its environment seemed to be coming to fruition. With an eye for symbolism, President Nixon chose New Year's Day 1970 for signing the National Environmental Policy Act into law. The new law was brief, as federal legislation goes, but its purpose was immensely broad: "To declare a national policy which will encourage productivity and enjoyable harmony between man and his environment..." This decade, the President said, "absolutely must be the years when America pays its debts to the past by reclaiming the purity of its air, its water, and our living environment."

Since those words were voiced, an energy crisis has interceded, brought forth by an oil embargo and subsequent price increases. This has tended to divert national attention from environmental concerns to energy needs. And a new President has come to office vowing to put together a comprehensive energy program that stresses conservation and protection of the environment. President Carter, with his own touch of symbolism, used solar heating rather than fossil fuel to keep warm while reviewing his inaugural parade.

At this time, Carter thus offers a new promise. But how well or badly has the promise of 1970 been kept? And, by extension, how does the record of the past bear on prospects for the future? This compilation of 10 Editorial Research Reports published during the past two years appraises many of the outstanding ecological, environmental and energy issues that have arisen and are still being debated. These include solar energy, nuclear waste disposal, the ozone controversy, pollution-control cost, environmental policy, and a host of related matters. Their intent is to unravel the complexities involved and make the issues more understandable to the public rather than to provide a scorecard of wins and losses. They do, *in toto,* make an assessment from which the reader may decide if the nation is doing what it should and as fast as it should.

Hoyt Gimlin
Editor

January 1977
Washington, D.C.

Solar Energy

by

John Hamer

**Nov. 12
1976**

SOLAR ENERGY

S OLAR ENERGY is by far the most abundant energy source
available to earth. The sun generates such an enormous
amount of energy that the facts and figures are almost in-
comprehensible. Only an infinitesimal fraction of the sun's radiant energy strikes this planet, but our share still equals
about 180 trillion kilowatts of electricity, or more than 25,000
times the world's present industrial power capacity. A few com-
parisons help to illustrate the awesome potential of solar energy.
The energy in the sunlight falling on the surface of Lake Erie in
a single day is greater than current annual U.S. energy consumption. The amount of solar radiation striking only 1 per cent
of the nation's land area each year is more than projected
national energy needs to the year 2000. The solar energy
reaching the surface of the entire United States annually is
greater than the total amount of fossil-fuel energy that, scientists say, will *ever* be extracted in this country.

The sun is already the indirect source of most of the energy
used on earth—from wood, wind and falling water to the coal,
oil and natural gas deposits formed centuries ago. But today,
with fossil-fuel resources rapidly being depleted, nuclear energy
plagued by cost and safety problems, and hydropower and
geothermal resources limited, interest in wider use of solar
energy is soaring. Solar power is seen as the clean, safe,
pollution-free and virtually inexhaustible energy source that
can meet the nation's—and the world's—energy supply needs
for the foreseeable future. A wide variety of technologies are being pursued, from direct use of solar energy to heat water and
buildings or generate electricity to indirect use through the
wind, ocean thermal layers or bioconversion of organic material
(see boxes, pp. 6 and 8).

But there are many problems. For one thing, sunlight is so dif-
fuse that collecting it and concentrating it present serious difficulties. Solar energy varies greatly with latitude, season, time
of day and weather conditions. Moreover, it cannot be converted
to useful power at 100 per cent efficiency, and it cannot be
stored easily for later use or transported to other areas. There
are numerous technical problems with most existing solar-
energy equipment, although progress has been rapid in recent
years and more refinements or scientific breakthroughs seem

3

imminent. Perhaps the greatest barriers to the acceptance of solar energy are political, social and economic. But none of these problems appears insoluble and it is increasingly likely that solar energy will emerge in the decades ahead as a major energy source for the United States and for other nations.

The unanswered questions are: How much will this energy cost and how soon will it be available? So far solar energy has not been economically competitive with cheap fossil fuels. And the future cost of solar energy is even more unpredictable than the price of oil, which has risen far beyond most expectations in recent years. As for availability, estimates vary. Proponents of solar energy say it could meet 50 to 100 per cent of the nation's energy needs by the end of the century, while skeptics contend it will provide only 5 to 10 per cent. The Energy Research and Development Administration, which has primary responsibility for federal solar-energy programs, is in the middle, predicting that solar energy will provide about 25 per cent of the nation's needs by the year 2020.

Existing Uses for Heating Water and Buildings

The first widespread use of solar energy in this country probably will be for heating water and for heating—and possibly cooling—buildings. Solar water heaters have been around for decades and many are still in use today. They are fairly simple devices, and most units work about the same way. A sheet of metal—often copper—and a series of metal tubes are painted black to absorb the sunlight, then covered by glass to trap the heat like a greenhouse. The unit is mounted on the roof, facing the sun. Water is pumped through the tubes where it collects heat, then is stored in an insulated tank much like conventional hot-water heaters. The water temperature commonly reaches 100 to 200 degrees on sunny days. The devices also can be used to heat water for swimming pools.

For space heating, the principle is similar. The sun's heat is transferred either to water or to air, which is then pumped or blown into a heating system's radiators or ducts. The heat can be stored in hot-water tanks or in a bed of hot rocks for release at night or in bad weather. At the beginning of this decade only a handful of homes and buildings in the United States had solar-heating units, but today there are more than 200 and new systems are being installed all the time. Many more are in the planning stages. Solar energy systems now are operating in private homes, government buildings, commercial establishments and public schools. Technically at least, solar energy also can be used for air-conditioning systems that, much like a refrigerator, pump a coolant. But more research is needed to improve their efficiency.

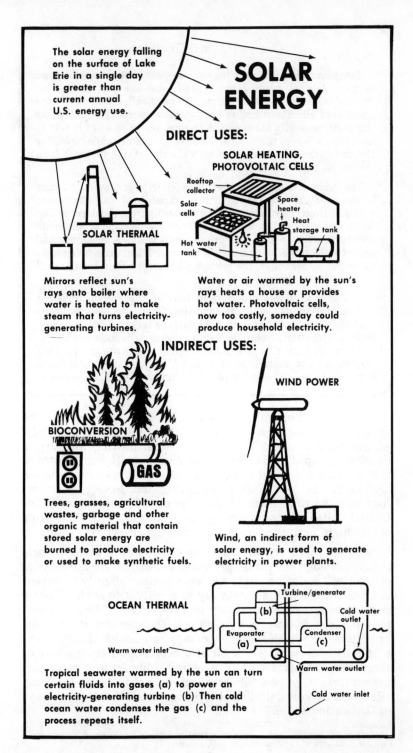

The solar energy falling on the surface of Lake Erie in a single day is greater than current annual U.S. energy use.

SOLAR ENERGY

DIRECT USES:

SOLAR HEATING, PHOTOVOLTAIC CELLS

Rooftop collector

Solar cells

Space heater

Heat storage tank

Hot water tank

SOLAR THERMAL

Mirrors reflect sun's rays onto boiler where water is heated to make steam that turns electricity-generating turbines.

Water or air warmed by the sun's rays heats a house or provides hot water. Photovoltaic cells, now too costly, someday could produce household electricity.

INDIRECT USES:

WIND POWER

BIOCONVERSION

GAS

Trees, grasses, agricultural wastes, garbage and other organic material that contain stored solar energy are burned to produce electricity or used to make synthetic fuels.

Wind, an indirect form of solar energy, is used to generate electricity in power plants.

OCEAN THERMAL

Turbine/generator

Cold water outlet

Evaporator (a)

Condenser (c)

(b)

Warm water inlet

Warm water outlet

Cold water inlet

Tropical seawater warmed by the sun can turn certain fluids into gases (a) to power an electricity-generating turbine (b) Then cold ocean water condenses the gas (c) and the process repeats itself.

Ocean Thermal Gradients

Temperature differences between sea water at the surface and at great depths—ocean thermal gradients—are another indirect form of solar energy. This source has been called potentially the greatest of all. About half of the radiant solar energy that strikes the earth annually lands in the tropics, where most of it acts to heat the surface of the oceans. This energy can be tapped by using the sun's stored heat together with the stored cold in water from the ocean depths *(see p. 5)*.

The process is fairly simple: An electricity-generating turbine is installed offshore in a facility capable of drawing warm seawater from the surface or colder water up from the depths. The warm water is used to warm a fluid such as propane or ammonia and turn it into a gas. The gas expands inside a container and provides the power to operate the turbine. Then, upon being cooled by the colder water, the gas again becomes a fluid to be reused over and over again.

The idea first was proposed in 1881 by the French physicist Arsene d'Arsonval, and an experimental model was built by Georges Claude of France in 1929, but the technology has received little attention since. The National Science Foundation has estimated that by the year 2000 thermal gradients in the Gulf Stream off the eastern coast of the United States alone could generate 5 per cent or more of the energy needed in this country.

William A. Shurcliff, a Harvard University physicist who makes an annual survey of solar-heated buildings in the United States, wrote last February: "A solar-heating industry is developing rapidly. Hardly a week goes by without the formation of a new company eager to sell collectors or associated equipment. Several giant corporations, too, have tossed their hats into the ring. Already there are over 40 companies in the United States offering water-type collectors for the solar heating of buildings, and there are a dozen offering air-type collectors."[1]

None of these ventures can be considered a great success today, although the future prospects are bright. Manufacturers of rooftop collector systems, each using slightly different equipment, are trying constantly to modify it to achieve better performance, longer durability and lower cost. "The competition involves, mainly, petty details," Shurcliff wrote. "No new principles of physics are expected, or sought. Rather, the emphasis is on salvaging a bit of otherwise lost energy here or there, reducing corrosion of a certain aluminum component, preventing a plastic sheet from warping or discoloring, eliminating a valve, finding cheaper materials and cheaper ways of fabricating them."

[1] William A. Shurcliff, "Active-Type Solar Heating Systems for Houses: A Technology in Ferment," *Bulletin of the Atomic Scientists,* February 1976, p. 30.

The solar-heating industry today has been compared to the automobile industry at the beginning of the century, waiting for a breakthrough that will bring rapid sales growth. However, it was mass production that enabled auto manufacturing to expand so rapidly, and most of the components of solar systems already are being mass produced. What will really help the industry are continued price increases for fuel oil, natural gas and electricity. The initial installation cost of solar units still is so high that it takes at least five and often 10 to 15 years before the cost is offset by savings on utility bills. As conventional utility costs increase, solar equipment will become more attractive economically.

There is hope for savings and efficiency in the combination of solar units with conventional systems. The heat pump, an electric-powered device already used in about one million American homes for heating and cooling, can be combined with solar rooftop collectors to lower heating bills significantly. The largest solar-heated building in the world, at New Mexico State University in Las Cruces, has such a system.

Converting Sunlight to Electricity; Cost Factors

Solar researchers also are giving considerable attention to the generation of electricity, especially since electricity is expected to provide more than half of this country's energy needs by 1985, compared to 25 per cent today. The two principal methods of converting sunlight to electricity are (1) through the use of photovoltaics, or solar cells, and (2) solar thermal conversion, the use of focused sunlight to heat water and drive steam turbines in an electric-power plant. The technology is not sufficiently advanced to make either method economically competitive with conventional ways of producing electricity. But the potential is great.

Photovoltaic cells have been used in America's space program for many years to provide energy in satellites, but the cost is extremely high. The Skylab space station ran entirely on solar cells, but at a cost of about $300,000 a kilowatt. Less intricate systems can be operated on earth for about $20,000 a kilowatt, still too high for all uses except in isolated places such as offshore oil rigs or remote communications stations. Still, the cost of solar cells has fallen to under $20 a watt from $200 a watt only five years ago, and further decreases are expected, since the technology is somewhat similar to the solid-state technology that has greatly reduced the cost of electronic calculators.

Solar cells have no moving parts. They consist mainly of two thin layers of material, one of them a semiconductor such as silicon and the other a metal such as aluminum or silver. A semiconductor can be treated so that when light strikes it

7

Energy From Bioconversion

A possible use of solar energy is the transformation of trees, plants and other organic material into useful power, a process known as bioconversion. Wood and dry animal manure have been burned for centuries as a small-scale source of heat, but today researchers are suggesting large-scale projects to produce electricity or gases for commercial or industrial use. The present annual production of "biomass" around the world is about 100 billion dry tons, which has an energy equivalent about six times greater than current energy use worldwide.

Converting this material into useful power is theoretically feasible, although the technology remains to be demonstrated practically. The National Science Foundation has recommended that pilot plants be built and tested using several bioconversion techniques, including the direct combustion of trees, certain grasses and other plants to make steam in electric power plants, and the conversion of agricultural wastes, municipal refuse, human sewage and animal wastes into methane gas or methyl alcohol.

Union Electric Co. in St. Louis already is using shredded garbage mixed with coal in power plants, and wastes in Baltimore and San Diego are being subjected to pyrolisis (chemical change induced by heat) to yield gases, oil and char for use as boiler, home-heating and motor fuels.

electrons flow across the two layers—the so-called photovoltaic effect—and generate current. This current is drawn off in wires to operate electric motors, light bulbs or other devices. Today photovoltaic flashlights, radios and television sets are available, but their price is much higher than their conventional counterparts. A panel of solar cells measuring about 10 feet by 40 feet could provide all the electricity needed by the average home, but it would cost more than $100,000.

Solar cells are expensive to manufacture because they are made from chemically pure silicon crystals that are sliced into ultrathin wafers by a precision, labor-intensive process. However, several companies are experimenting with methods of making long silicon crystal rods or ribbons that could be sliced in a mass-production technique. Solarex Corp. of Rockville, Md., and Mobil Tyco Laboratories of Waltham, Mass., are investing heavily in solar cells in the hope of making a research breakthrough. "The day may arrive when solar cells are delivered to a house like rolls of roofing paper, tacked on, and plugged into the wiring, making the home its own power station," John L. Wilhelm wrote in *National Geographic*.[2]

---

[2] John L. Wilhelm, "Solar Energy, the Ultimate Powerhouse," *National Geographic*, March 1976.

Another ambitious plan for using solar cells is put forward by Peter Glaser of Arthur D. Little Inc., an industrial consulting firm in Cambridge, Mass. Glaser suggests that a huge satellite in orbit could use solar panels several miles long to generate electricity and beam it back to earth in the form of microwaves to a receiving station. The microwaves would be converted into alternating-current electricity and distributed through utility grids. The plan, though futuristic, is technically feasible and is under study by such companies as Boeing, Grumman, Textron and Raytheon. Assuming the development of new space vehicles and methods for construction in orbit, Glaser believes the system could become operational by the year 2000.

Solar thermal conversion is still in a developmental stage in the United States, although small systems began operation in France and Mexico this year. They focus the sun's heat on a boiler to produce steam to run turbines that power electric generators. The drawback to this system is that it requires a lot of land to place the large number of mirrors or other reflectors needed to concentrate solar energy. It takes about one square mile of land to hold enough solar collectors to produce 25,000 kilowatts of electricity. At that rate, about 5,000 square miles of land in the sunny Southwest would be needed to generate enough electricity for the United States today. However, solar proponents point out that agriculture consumes 500,000 square miles of land and produces only about 1 per cent of the nation's energy needs in the form of food.

A number of ideas have been advanced to improve heat efficiency and lessen the need for land. Professor and Mrs. Aden Meinel of the University of Arizona have proposed a solar-thermal system using special lenses to focus sunlight onto chemically coated, nitrogen-filled pipes. The solar farm, as they call it, would occupy 25 square miles and produce 1,000 megawatts of electricity. Another research team, sponsored by the University of Minnesota and Honeywell Inc., has proposed to use a parabolic reflector to concentrate sunlight into air-filled heating pipes. Other researchers are concentrating on what they call "total energy" systems, where solar-thermal plants would make electricity for industrial parks, shopping centers, military bases or even entire towns, while the leftover heat would be used to warm and cool buildings and to run some kinds of equipment.

Wind Power as Indirect Use of Solar Energy

An indirect form of solar energy that can be used to produce electricity is the wind. Wind is created by the earth's "heat engine"—air is heated by the sun's rays and cooled by their absence. The World Meteorological Organization has estimated wind power available at favorable sites around the world at some 20 million megawatts, or more than 40 times the present electric-generating capacity throughout the nation. Wind power has been used for centuries to sail ships and turn windmills. The first windmills appeared in the seventh century A.D. and have been used ever since to pump water, mill grain and—in this century—to produce electricity. In 1941 the world's largest windmill—110 feet high with 175-foot-diameter blades—was built atop Grandpa's Knob near Rutland, Vt. It produced 1.3 megawatts of electricity until it was shut down in 1945.

A joint committee of the National Science Foundation and the National Aeronautics and Space Administration recently suggested that wind power could produce 1.5 trillion kilowatts of electricity by the year 2000 if a development program were actively pursued. That is almost as much electricity as the amount consumed annually in the United States. Today, many experiments to harness wind power are under way in this country and abroad. Engineers are using advanced aeronautical concepts in their search for a slender, lightweight blade that will allow windmill shafts to spin quickly in light winds and be sturdy enough to stand high winds. Last year the federal government began conducting experiments with a 100-kilowatt wind turbine at Sandusky, Ohio. The unit stands 100 feet tall on a steel tower and its propeller blades span 125 feet.

The main problem with windmills for electric-power generation is the expense of construction. At least $5,000 is required to build even a small windmill capable of producing electricity. Consequently, the electricity is likely to be costlier than if obtained from conventional sources. Also, an array of windmills large enough to produce electricity for an entire town or city would take up an enormous amount of space and create a kind of visual pollution of the landscape.

Even so, several wind-power proposals have received considerable attention in recent years. One of the most ambitious is offered by Professor William E. Heronemus of the University of Massachusetts, who suggests that huge windmills be built on floating towers or platforms in the oceans offshore. These would be out of sight from land and could generate large amounts of electricity that could be cabled ashore or, Heronemus suggests, used to separate distilled sea water into hydrogen and oxygen in an electrolytic process. The hydrogen then could be piped or shipped ashore to be burned in electric-generating plants, or someday perhaps used in homes and automobiles in place of natural gas and gasoline.

Progress Toward Tapping Sun Power

D IRECT USE of the sun's energy has been a goal of creative minds through history. Archimedes, the Greek inventor and mathematician, reportedly used the bright metal shields of a thousand soldiers to focus the sun's rays and set fire to 'an invading Roman fleet during the Second Punic War.[3] A similar tactic was said to have been used during the siege of Constantinople in 626 A.D.[4] During the following centuries, a few experimenters duplicated Archimedes' legendary feat on a smaller scale, setting fire to woodpiles.

In the late 18th century, the French chemist Antoine Lavoisier built a solar furnace that used two large, hollow lenses filled with alcohol to increase their refractive power. The device concentrated the sun's rays so efficiently that Lavoisier was able to melt metals, including steel and platinum, for research purposes. French inventors continued to lead the way in solar experimentation, devising several solar-powered steam engines in the 19th century. One of them operated a printing press that turned out a newspaper appropriately entitled *Le Soleil* (The Sun).[5]

In the United States, the Swedish-American inventor John Ericsson, designer of the Union's ironclad warship *Monitor,* also designed a number of solar-powered engines later in the 19th century. They were the most efficient solar devices built up to that time, but Ericsson concluded that they were still too costly and complex, so he converted them to run on inexpensive coal and gas. A number of other solar-powered engines were built in the early 1900s by various American inventors, but these also proved impractical or uneconomical because of the wide availability of fossil fuels.[6]

One solar device that did find a large market was the solar water heater. In the first half of this century, tens of thousands of these units were manufactured and sold in California, Florida and other sunny states. Most of them employed a rooftop collector consisting of blackened copper tubes in a metal box under a pane of glass, and many had insulated storage tanks to keep water hot overnight. As late as 1950, it was estimated that 50,-000 such heaters were in operation in Miami alone. But by the early 1970s, because of competition from cheap natural gas and fuel oil, the industry had virtually disappeared.

---

[3] According to the Greek historian Galen, this occurred at Syracuse in 212 B.C. However, Livy and Plutarch do not mention the event in their histories.
[4] D. S. Halacy Jr., *The Coming Age of Solar Energy* (1963), p. 197.
[5] Hans Rau, *Solar Energy* (1964), p. 46.
[6] For a detailed historical review, see Wilson Clark, *Energy for Survival* (1974), pp. 361-374.

Solar water pumps and water distillers also found considerable success. From 1870 to about 1910 solar energy provided fresh water for a remote mining area in Chile. Windmills pumped brine into a series of glass-covered troughs where water evaporated and condensed on panes of glass, then trickled down into collection channels. Some 50,000 square feet of solar collectors produced 5,000 gallons of pure water per day in the summertime.[7] An example of a successful water pump was that on the Pasadena Ostrich Farm in California. A large reflector heated water in a steam boiler and powered a pump that raised about 1,400 gallons of water a minute. The installation was famous nationwide in the early 1900s.

Perhaps the best-known American in the field was Dr. Charles Greeley Abbot of the Smithsonian Institution, who has been called the "venerable dean of America's solar scientists."[8] Abbot designed solar cookers, parabolic concentrators, water distillers and steam engines, and was the oldest living U.S. patent holder until his death in 1973 at the age of 101. Another pioneer was Dr. Robert Goddard, who took out several patents on solar-powered devices before be began to concentrate on rocketry in the late 1920s and helped usher in the space age half a century later.

Present Uses of Solar Energy in Other Nations

The use of solar equipment did not die out in many other countries as it did in the United States. In Australia, Japan and Israel, for example, the use of solar water heaters is widespread today. In Australia, the units are used primarily in rural areas, but in Japan and Israel they are found in cities as well. In recent years there have been estimates that more than 200,000 solar water heaters have been installed in Japan and more than 100,000 in Israel.

France leads the world in the large-scale use of concentrated solar energy for scientific research and electricity generation. The French scientist Felix Trombe, a leading solar experimenter, started building solar furnaces in the Pyrenees in the 1950s, and in 1970 completed an eight-story parabolic reflector that heats a furnace to 6,000 degrees Fahrenheit. It has been used primarily to melt metals, ceramics and other materials for research purposes. But in October 1976, the installation was used to power a steam turbine to produce about 100 kilowatts of electricity that were fed into an electric power grid. It was the first time solar energy ever had been used in a commercial utility system.

The French plan to expand the program in an effort to reduce

---

[7] *Ibid.*, p. 364.
[8] By Wilson Clark, p. 367.

the nation's heavy dependence on imported oil and gas. "If there are problems, we'll have to perfect the operation," said Claude Bienvenu of Electricité de France, the national power company. "We have to learn how to use the sun."[9] Also in October, an American corporation, Martin-Marietta, successfully tested a 10-ton, 1,000-kilowatt steam boiler at the French installation in the Pyrenees as part of a program sponsored by the Energy Research and Development Administration (ERDA).[10]

A similar solar-thermal installation began operation in Guanajuato, Mexico, in January 1976, although it does not produce electricity commercially. The facility uses an array of flat collectors to heat water and power a turbine that provides 30 kilowatts of electricity to run two water pumps. These pumps supply a million liters (264,200 gallons) of pure water daily, and the Mexican government plans to build 10 additional solar-powered water-pumping facilities, as well as electricity-generating plants.[11]

Federal Research Effort After Oil Embargo

Despite considerable interest in solar energy among scientists, inventors and entrepreneurs during much of this century, widespread solar development has not occurred in the United States. The main problem has been the high cost of equipment. In addition, there has been continued opposition to solar power from the oil, coal and natural gas industries, which saw their interests threatened. Also, since World War II the nuclear-power lobby has become a strong force in favor of the "peaceful atom" and has opposed substantial commitments to solar energy.

Nonetheless, there have been numerous attempts to encourage American solar development in recent decades. The first federal solar energy bill was introduced in Congress in 1951, dealing with wind power. In 1952, President Truman's Materials Policy Commission issued the famous "Paley Report," named for its chairman, William S. Paley of the Columbia Broadcasting System. This remarkable document strongly recommended solar energy as an alternative to fossil fuels, and predicted that 13 million buildings could be heated by solar units by 1975. It said solar power could meet 10 per cent of the nation's energy needs if the technology were developed aggressively. Needless to say, that optimistic forecast did not come true.

During the next two decades, 10 more bills having to do with solar energy were introduced in Congress, but none passed.

---

[9] Quoted in *Business Week*, Oct. 11, 1976, p. 29.
[10] *The New York Times*, Oct. 18, 1976.
[11] Jeannie Anderson, "Mexico Outstrips U.S. in Preparation of Solar Future," *Critical Mass* (a publication of the Citizens' Movement for Safe and Efficient Energy), May 1976, p. 14.

Then in 1973, the Arab oil embargo suddenly brought solar energy to the forefront of federal energy planning. "The following months were a nightmare of gasoline shortages and a parallel feverish congressional activity toward solar energy legislation," Dan Halacy, an aide to Sen. Paul J. Fannin (R Ariz.) said in a recent report.[12] "Almost overnight solar acquired the sex appeal of a manned space shot and a high promise as the salvation of an energy-starved constituency. To be against solar legislation was practically unthinkable...."

As many as 24 solar-related bills were introduced in the 93rd Congress during 1973 and 1974, and in the fall of 1974 two of the measures became law. The Solar Heating and Cooling Demonstration Act of 1974 established a five-year, $60-million program that directed the National Aeronautics and Space Administration to carry out solar projects and authorized the Department of Housing and Urban Development to supervise the installation of solar units in public and private buildings. The Solar Energy Research, Development and Demonstration Act of 1974 authorized $77-million for a wide variety of programs including a solar resources appraisal, a solar information data bank, demonstration of eight solar projects and establishment of a Solar Energy Research Institute.[13]

In the 94th Congress (1975-76), more than 50 solar measures were introduced, nearly half of which offered incentives for the rapid development of solar equipment by individuals. Although most of the bills did not pass, the clear indication of support for solar development had its effect on budget authorizations. While only $1.4-million in federal funds were spent on solar research and development in 1970, the first budget of the Energy Research and Development Administration contained $40-million for solar projects in 1975. Congressional appropriations topped $100-million in fiscal year 1976 and reached $290-million in fiscal 1977 for various solar programs. "[S]olar proponents find it difficult to believe such good fortune," Halacy wrote. "Indeed, some maintain that they will believe it only when the money actually has been spent...."

In addition, other federal agencies are actively supporting solar projects. The Department of Defense has begun to install solar heating systems at various military bases. The General Services Administration, the government's biggest landlord, is doing the same for certain federal buildings around the nation. The Department of Agriculture has set up a model solar home in South Carolina and is explaining the uses of solar energy through its Extension Service. The Forest Service has used solar

---

[12] "Federal Solar Legislation," a paper presented to the Consumer Conference on Solar Energy Development, Albuquerque, N.M., Oct. 2, 1976.

[13] For details of bills, see *Congressional Quarterly Almanac 1974*, pp. 752-757.

energy at administration buildings, remote maintenance structures and even outhouses. The space agency has installed a solar-powered refrigerator on an Indian reservation in Arizona.

Plan for U.S. Solar Energy Research Institute

One of the most significant federal commitments to solar energy in the long run may be the establishment of a Solar Energy Research Institute (SERI). The Energy Research and Development Administration announced in October that it had postponed the final selection of a site for the new institute until next March. The decision was due to have been announced in December. Competition is fierce among the states for this "research plum."

According to ERDA's official request for proposals, the research institute's mission will be to support the federal solar energy program, help establish an "industrial base" and foster widespread use of solar equipment. During its first year, the institute will have a budget of $4-million to $6-million and a staff of 49 to 76 persons. The figures are expected to grow considerably in subsequent years. About 20 proposals have been submitted by a wide variety of state, university, business and scientific groups. Among the leading contenders are:

Arizona. A state-sponsored Solar Energy Research Commission is working full-time to land SERI; the Battelle Memorial Institute of Columbus, Ohio, would manage and operate it.

California. The state-sanctioned effort is being funded by the Energy Resources, Conservation and Development Commission in connection with several universities.

Colorado. A statewide committee was appointed to prepare Colorado's proposal with the help of legislative appropriations and industry contributions.

Florida. A state energy task force has a full-time staff based at Cape Canaveral.

Michigan. The campaign is led by the Michigan Energy and Resource Research Association, a partnership of state government, universities and industries.

New England. The six New England states (Connecticut, Maine, Massachusetts, New Hampshire, Rhode Island and Vermont) have banded together in an effort supported by the New England Council, an organization of some 2,200 corporations, universities and government officials.

New Mexico. The first state to submit a proposal; it is backed by a group of universities and scientific laboratories in combination with the Stanford Research Institute.

New York. A site near the Brookhaven National Laboratory on Long Island was proposed by a state-university-business group.

Texas. El Paso, San Antonio and Houston all have submitted competing proposals without any state funding or coordination.

Uncertainty in Development Efforts

S OLAR ENERGY's future depends on a complex array of social, political and economic problems whose resolution cannot be predicted with certainty. The most encouraging signs of progress in solar energy today are in industry. More than 250 companies nationwide are involved in solar development, ranging from individual entrepreneurs working in their garages to huge corporations such as PPG Industries, Grumman, Owens-Illinois and subsidiaries of such giant oil companies as Exxon and Mobil. Sales of their products and services probably amount to less than $25-million annually now, but Arthur D. Little Inc., the Cambridge-based consulting firm, estimates that sales of water- and space-heating equipment alone may reach $1.3-billion a year by 1985.[14]

However, even some of solar energy's strongest proponents concede that many predictions of a bright future have been too rosy. "We're still enthusiastic, but we're becoming very realistic," Aden Meinel of the University of Arizona, architect of the "solar farm" concept, told a recent seminar.[15] "Solar sounds so easy to use, but you run into very practical problems. We got pack rats in one of our collectors, for instance, and that's pretty hard to predict on a computer. We've got to keep it in perspective. It needs time and patience."

Similarly, William A. Shurcliff of Harvard University, who annually surveys solar buildings in the United States, has written: "At least 80 per cent of the 200 or so solar-heated buildings that exist today have been uneconomic.... [T]he total lifetime cost of building the equipment and operating it for, say, 20 years is much greater than the money saved through reduction in amount of fuel or electrical power used—assuming that the costs of fuel and electrical power remain at today's levels. In most instances, the overall cost exceeds the overall benefit by a factor of two or three."[16] Nonetheless, Shurcliff believes that a few solar heating systems are "truly economic" and he remains "highly optimistic."

Another solar energy expert who expresses caution is A. I. Mlavsky, head of the Mobil Tyco Laboratories photovoltaic project. "There is a concept—it's engrained in the American ethos—that if you put enough guys and enough money to work on something, you can do anything," Mlavsky said. "It's baloney.... The solar field is a young field.... It's receiving a lot

---

[14] Andrew Tobias, "Solar Energy Now: Why Aren't We Using It More?" *New York,* May 31, 1976, p. 32.

[15] Quoted by Julie Tripp in *The Arizona Daily Star* of Tucson, Oct. 5, 1976.

[16] *Bulletin of the Atomic Scientists,* February 1976, p. 38.

of attention. It will not provide major solutions to our energy problems in a short time, and those—including myself—who sometimes get sucked into thinking that it will are wrong." Mlavsky contends that if the sun is meeting a "significant fraction" of the energy needs in 25 years, "we'll have done a hell of a job."[17]

Barriers of Building Codes and Housing Costs

Among the barriers to the development of solar energy are building codes, financing constraints, tax laws, construction methods and labor requirements. Alan S. Hirshberg, an engineer at California Institute of Technology, wrote recently: "[R]esearch indicates that even when solar space conditioning is economical, institutional barriers to its widespread acceptance will remain."[18] There are about 3,000 building code jurisdictions in the United States, many of them with conflicting regulations. These codes tend to limit the use of new methods and favor existing materials and practices. Few of the codes have yet been revised to list performance specifications for solar equipment. Fire codes also might apply to solar heating systems, requiring fire-resistant parts and adequate insulation around solar units. Health codes might apply to solar systems that used chemicals to transfer or store heat.

Financing limitations of home builders and buyers further inhibit the development of solar energy. The building industry and most home buyers operate on borrowed money, and the high initial construction costs of solar units can make it difficult—and expensive—to get construction or mortgage loans. "The industry is highly sensitive to initial investments (the first cost of its products), and the normal way to reduce the risk of high finance charges is to reduce initial capital requirements," Hirshberg wrote. "Solar devices which have lower operating costs but higher initial investment costs than other energy systems could be expected to meet industry resistance."

The U.S. building industry's general makeup also can be expected to slow solar development to some extent. It is a diverse, fragmented and highly independent industry composed of some 100,000 home builders, 90 per cent of whom produce fewer than 100 units each year. The nation's largest builders produce less than 1 per cent of the annual total. So a new technology such as solar energy must be accepted by an enormous number of individual builders and be integrated into existing distribution, sales and service systems. Also, the building industry embraces many crafts and trades, most of them with strong unions. Carpenters, plumbers, roofers, masons and electricians

---

[17] Quoted by Michael Harwood in *The New York Times Magazine*, March 16, 1975, p. 37.
[18] "Public Policy for Solar Heating and Cooling," *Bulletin of the Atomic Scientists*, October 1976, p. 38.

all might have a hand in the installation and servicing of solar systems. Especially complicated would be putting solar equipment into an existing home. This could entail tying into old pipes or excavating a basement to install a heat-storage tank. Even so, some unions see the development of solar energy as a means of increasing jobs.[19]

Another complexity is the question of "sun rights"—what to do if a neighbor's new building blocks the afternoon sun. "Protecting access to sunlight for purposes of solar heating and power generation is a subject awash with unsettled legal questions," two lawyers, Arnold W. Reitze Jr. and Glenn L. Reitze, have written.[20] English law provides a right to daylight, although it is not absolute, while American law is less clear on the subject. Even so, the Reitzes said that proposals to create an absolute right to solar radiation might do more harm than good, and are probably unconstitutional. "To ban shadows is to ban growth," they wrote. "[S]olar energy access legislation is simply not the proper means to attempt to implement no-growth policies, and such laws can be counterproductive to solar use."

Finally, there may be environmental problems associated with large-scale solar development. Efforts to build enormous solar-thermal conversion plants in the Southwest might arouse considerable opposition from local landowners or environmentalists. In the eastern states, the most likely sites for solar-electric plants would be valuable farm, forest or marsh lands. "Solar uses six times more land than nuclear power and that means six times as many battles for sites," R. C. Carlson of the Stanford Research Institute said in a recent paper.[21]

Central Role of the Nation's Electric Utility Industry

Another industry that may play a central role in the development of solar energy is the electric utility industry. This, too, is a diverse industry consisting of about 300 private, investor-owned utility companies that supply 75 per cent of the electricity in the United States and some 3,000 municipal and regional utilities and rural electric cooperatives that provide the remaining 25 per cent.[22] The nation's utilities are far from having a unified position on solar energy, but there probably has been more opposition than support.

On the other hand, some private utilities are investigating the possibility of ownership and control of solar equipment for residential and commercial buildings. The utility would install,

[19] See, for example, "Solar Power Systems," *The Machinist*, November 1976, p. 3. The magazine is published by the International Association of Machinists and Aerospace Workers.

[20] "Protecting a Place in the Sun," *Environment*, June 1976, p. 2.

[21] "Solar Energy: Has the Time Come?" a paper presented to the Consumer Conference on Solar Energy Development, Albuquerque, N.M., Oct. 2, 1976.

[22] See "Future of Utilities," *E.R.R.*, 1975 Vol. I, pp. 185-204.

own and maintain the system, while the homeowner, landlord or business owner would lease it from the utility and make a monthly payment to cover installation and financing costs, maintenance and profit. Public utilities could handle solar energy in much the same way, except the community at large would own the equipment and costs would be lower. Garry DeLoss, an energy specialist who works for Ralph Nader in Washington, D.C., has said: "I'm sympathetic to the idea of publicly owned utilities investing in solar equipment and private utility ownership is a place where the profit motive might be put to good use."

Tax Incentives to Purchase Solar Equipment

To some extent, the future of solar energy in the United States may be determined by tax incentives at federal, state and local levels to promote the use of solar energy. Alan S. Hirshberg has proposed incentives that include federal tax credits, low-interest loans and property tax abatement.

In the past few years, several states have provided property-tax incentives to homeowners to install solar equipment. Property taxes normally go up when home improvements increase assessed value, but the various state measures enable localities to exempt the homeowner from added property taxes on improvements resulting from the installation of solar equipment. According to the National Conference of State Legislatures, states that have passed such measures include Arizona, Colorado, Connecticut, Hawaii, Illinois, Indiana, Kansas, Maryland, Massachusetts, Michigan, Montana, New Hampshire, North Dakota, Oregon and South Dakota.

In addition, state income tax incentives for the use of solar devices are offered by Arizona, California, Hawaii, Idaho, Kansas, Michigan and New Mexico. Georgia, Texas and Vermont exempt solar equipment from state or local sales taxes. Fifteen states provide public funds for solar-energy research, development and promotion through grants to universities, nonprofit groups, public agencies or individuals who undertake specific projects. These states are Arizona, California, Colorado, Florida, Hawaii, Iowa, Maine, Michigan, Montana, Nevada, New Mexico, New York, North Carolina, Ohio and Virginia.

Nevertheless, both state and federal policies at present generally continue to favor fossil fuels and nuclear power over solar energy. In the end the question seems to be: Should the nation continue to deplete fossil fuel resources and expand its commitment to nuclear power, or must it encourage the rapid development of solar energy and other renewable sources? As the greatest energy source on earth, solar power is destined to have its day but no one can say how soon.

Selected Bibliography

Books

Behrman, Daniel, *Solar Energy: The Awakening Science,* Little, Brown & Co., 1976.
Clark, Wilson, *Energy for Survival,* Anchor Books, 1974.
Daniels, George, *Solar Homes and Sun Heating,* Harper & Row, 1976.
Halacy, D. S. Jr., *The Coming Age of Solar Energy,* Harper & Row, 1963.
Keyes, John, *The Solar Conspiracy,* Morgan & Morgan, 1975.
Meinel, Aden B. and Marjorie P., *Applied Solar Energy: An Introduction,* Addison-Wesley, 1976.
Rau, Hans, *Solar Energy,* D. T. Duffin, 1964.

Articles

Abelson, Philip H., "Energy From Biomass," *Science,* March 26, 1976.
Arrandale, Tom, "Solar Energy: Funding Level Debated," *Congressional Quarterly Weekly Report,* April 24, 1976.
Bos, Piet B., "Solar Realities," *EPRI Journal,* February 1976.
Bulletin of the Atomic Scientists, selected issues.
Environment, selected issues.
Faltermayer, Edmund, "Solar Energy Is Here, But It's Not Yet Utopia," *Fortune,* February 1976.
Gilmore, C. P., "Sunpower!" *Saturday Review,* Oct. 30, 1976.
Harwood, Michael, "Energy From Our Star Will Compete With Oil, Natural Gas, Coal and Uranium—But Not Soon," *The New York Times Magazine,* March 16, 1975.
Northcross, Mark, "Who Will Own the Sun?" *The Progressive,* April 1976.
Tobias, Andrew, "Solar Energy Now: Why Aren't We Using It More?" *New York,* May 31, 1976.
Wilhelm, John L., "Solar Energy, the Ultimate Powerhouse," *National Geographic,* March 1976.

Studies and Reports

Carlson, R. C., "Solar Energy: Has the Time Come?" Stanford Research Institute, October 1976.
Eisenhard, Robert M., "A Survey of State Legislation Relating to Solar Energy," National Bureau of Standards, April 1976.
Editorial Research Reports, "New Energy Sources," 1973 Vol. I, p. 185.
Hillhouse, Karin Halvorson, "Solar Energy—Its Environmental Dimensions," Environmental Law Institute, October 1976.
National Conference of State Legislatures, "Turning Toward the Sun, Volume One," January 1976.
Roberson, J. Bob, "The Utility Role in Solar Commercialization," Southern California Edison, October 1976.

N UCLEAR WASTE DISPOSAL

by

Sandra Stencel

Dec. 3
1976

NUCLEAR WASTE DISPOSAL

THE NUCLEAR INDUSTRY is beset by a host of unsolved problems—preventing accidents, protecting plants from terrorist attacks, making nuclear energy economically feasible, preventing the secret diversion of nuclear material into weapons. One of the most unsettling problems concerns the handling of radioactive wastes from the federal government's weapons program and from commercial nuclear reactors. Although such wastes have been accumulating for more than 30 years, there still is no plan for their permanent disposal.

Both critics and defenders of nuclear power agree that the problem must be solved. President-elect Jimmy Carter, himself a nuclear engineer, told a United Nations conference on nuclear energy on May 13 that it was time for the United States "to cut through the indecision and debate about the long-term storage of radioactive wastes and start doing something about it." As a first step, Carter said, the United States "could begin by preparing all high-level wastes currently produced from our military programs for permanent disposal."

Nuclear power advocates generally contend that the technology necessary for the safe management of nuclear wastes already exists. H. A. Bethe, a Nobel prize-winning physicist wrote early this year: "It seems to me virtually certain that a suitable permanent storage site will be found."[1] Dixy Lee Ray, former chairman of the old Atomic Energy Commission and the newly elected governor of Washington, said in a recent interview: "Technologies do exist for handling the waste, for being able to take care of the waste, for being able to store the waste...safely and completely for as long as it needs to be done."[2] According to Ray, "The United States has not decided which of several technologies it will use, because we don't have to start doing anything with the waste from nuclear power plants until nearly the middle of the 1980s." That means, she went on to say, "We have got at least five years still to conduct research and maybe improve the techniques that are available today."

Opponents of nuclear power insist that the United States halt nuclear power-plant construction until a foolproof method for

---

[1] H.A. Bethe, "The Necessity of Fission Power," *Scientific American*, January 1976, p. 28.
[2] Henry B. Burnett, "Interview With Dixie Lee Ray," *Skeptic*, July-August 1976, p. 47.

disposing of nuclear wastes is developed. Some doubt that such a solution will ever be found. Consumer activist Ralph Nader, one of the most outspoken critics of nuclear power, told the Joint Congressional Economic Committee last year: "There are as many solutions to permanent radioactive waste disposal as there are nuclear proponents, but when each solution approaches implementation, it proves unworkable." Nader's solution: "Stop producing waste. We don't need nuclear power." The fact is, however, that a moratorium on nuclear energy development would not eliminate the waste problem. Safe disposal methods still must be found for those wastes already in existence and those that will continue to be generated by the government's nuclear weapons program.

Source of Atomic Waste Across the Nation

Although radioactive wastes are generated at each stage of the nuclear fuel cycle *(see opposite page)*, the most dangerous wastes are created in the operation of the reactors. Various decay products of nuclear fission build up in the fuel as the reaction proceeds and soon begin to interfere with fission activity. Because of this, and because the uranium fuel is gradually being consumed, about a third of the fuel in a reactor must be removed each year and replaced by new fuel. The spent fuel can be processed to recover usable uranium and plutonium, but a lethal residue of liquid waste remains.

The government already has accumulated about 75 million gallons of highly toxic, long-lasting radioactive waste from its weapons program, and 7.5 million gallons are added each year. Most of this waste (72 per cent) is stored at the Hanford Reservation near Richland, Wash. The rest is stored at the Savannah River Plant near Aiken, S.C. (25 per cent) and the Idaho National Engineering Laboratory near Idaho Falls, Idaho (3 per cent).[3]

Large quantities of commercially generated high-level wastes are piling up at the 60 nuclear power reactors operating across the nation. In theory, the used fuel was supposed to be shipped to commercial reprocessing plants where uranium and plutonium would be recovered before the remaining waste was turned over to the government for permanent disposal. But the country's three commercial reprocessing plants have encountered financial and technical problems, and there are serious doubts that they will actually go into service *(see p. 39)*.

In the meantime, spent fuel continues to accumulate. The Nuclear Regulatory Commission estimated that in 1975 there were 6,047 spent fuel assemblies stored in cooling ponds at the nation's nuclear power plants. In addition, about 600,000

---

[3] "Progress, Problems Cited in Report to Congress," *Nuclear News*, February 1975, p. 44.

The Nuclear Fuel Cycle

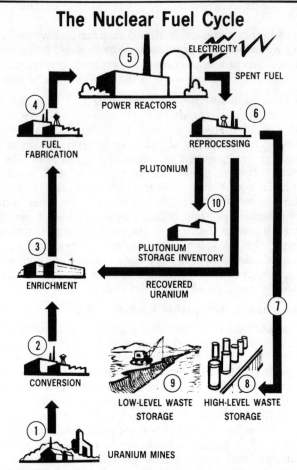

ELECTRICITY

⑤

SPENT FUEL

POWER REACTORS

④

FUEL
FABRICATION

⑥

REPROCESSING

PLUTONIUM

⑩

③

PLUTONIUM
STORAGE INVENTORY

ENRICHMENT

RECOVERED
URANIUM

⑦

②

CONVERSION

⑨

LOW-LEVEL WASTE
STORAGE

⑧

HIGH-LEVEL WASTE
STORAGE

①

URANIUM MINES

1. Mining and milling of ore to obtain raw uranium, called yellowcake, generates large quantities of low-level wastes called uranium tailings.
2. Removal of the impurities from the yellowcake and conversion.
3. Enrichment of the uranium from step 2 to a level suitable for power reactor fuel.
4. Conversion of the uranium from step 3 to leave a powder, which is fabricated into fuel elements for the power reactor.
5. Insertion of the fuel elements into the power reactor; operation of the reactor to produce electricity; removal of the spent or partially consumed fuel from the reactor; and storage of the highly radioactive spent fuel rods in cooling tanks at power plant.
6. Reprocessing of the spent fuel to separate unconsumed fuel from the radioactive wastes for future recycle.
7. Solidification of high-level liquid wastes left over after reprocessing to reduce the risks of accidental release and allow for permanent disposal.
8. Storage of high-level radioactive wastes for indefinite periods of time.
9. Burial of contaminated equipment, clothing and other low-level wastes.
10. Plutonium storage; recycling of recovered uranium.

chapman   **Source: Energy Research and Development Administration**

25

gallons of highly radioactive liquid commercial waste is being stored at a reprocessing plant near West Valley, N.Y., that has been closed. According to current projections, commercial high-level wastes could amount to 60 million gallons by the year 2000.

High-level radioactive wastes are classified as either fission products or fission byproducts.[4] Although they have different properties and life spans, all must be isolated from the human environment for hundreds of years. In general, fission products have shorter toxic lives than fission byproducts. The most troublesome fission products, strontium-90 and cesium-137, have half-lives[5] of about 30 years—which means that they remain dangerous for 600 to 1,000 years. On the other hand, the fission byproduct plutonium-239 has a half-life of over 24,000 years, which means that it must be isolated from the biosphere for nearly 500,000 years. And because current reprocessing techniques do not physically separate the fission products from the fission byproducts, all high-level nuclear wastes must be contained for nearly half a million years.

Questions About Acceptable Radiation Risks

The special hazards posed by radioactive wastes result from the emission of radiation, which even at low levels is injurious to animal life. Radiation cannot be detected by human senses except in massive doses. Its effects are cumulative and may not be evident for some time—as in the case of cancer development or genetic damage. Radioactive materials can be hazardous to humans either as a result of direct contact, ingestion or inhalation, or indirectly through environmental contamination. Plutonium-239 generally is considered the most dangerous element in high-level waste. Although so far as is known it has never caused human death or injury, as little as 0.0000001 ounce has caused lung cancer in dogs when inhaled as fine particles.[6]

Sheldon Novick, in his book *The Careless Atom* (1969), wrote: "In other forms of air and water pollution, we had to reach the point of real disaster before beginning to think of control. This must not be allowed to happen with radioactive wastes—once entered on their winding course through the environment, radioactive isotopes are out of reach of man's control. The damage, once done, is irremediable."[7]

---

[4] Fission products are the smaller atomic fragments of the split uranium atoms. Fission byproducts are larger atoms formed when other, non-fissionable large atoms capture neutrons.

[5] A "half-life" is the period of time that must elapse before the radioactivity has been reduced, through decay, to 50 per cent of its former level. For example, a 30-year half-life means that after each 30-year period, one-half of the isotopes present at the beginning of the period will have decayed.

[6] See "Plutonium: Biomedical Research," *Science*, Feb. 22, 1974, p. 715.

[7] See also Terry Lash, "Citizens' Guide: The National Debate on the Handling of Radioactive Wastes From Nuclear Power Plants," Natural Resources Defense Council, November 1975, p. 16.

Despite the dangers posed by the accumulation of large quantities of highly radioactive materials, waste management has had a relatively low priority in nuclear development. Most technical people familiar with the subject regarded waste disposal as a difficult but soluble problem, and not a major obstacle to widespread adoption of nuclear power. According to Harvey Brooks, dean of engineering and applied physics at Harvard University, "[T]he nuclear community tended to look at waste disposal as a non-urgent problem which would be solved in due course as the accumulation of wastes from commercial nuclear power made the problem more imminent."

The problem, Brooks said, was that the technical community failed to pass its confidence on to the public. Speaking at an international symposium in Denver sponsored by the Energy Research and Development Administration (ERDA) in July 1976, Brooks said government inaction in waste management "left the public with the impression that the technical managers didn't know what they were doing or where they were ultimately headed." This credibility must be restored, he added, because if nuclear energy should "ultimately prove socially unacceptable, it will be primarily because of the waste disposal problem." The uncertainties surrounding the nuclear waste question have been dramatized by several incidents in the last six months:

The U.S. Court of Appeals for the District of Columbia ruled on July 21 that the Nuclear Regulatory Commission must consider in more detail the environmental effects of nuclear waste disposal before issuing permits to construct or operate nuclear power plants. In response, the NRC announced on Aug. 13 that it would issue no new operating licenses or construction permits until it had completed a new review of the waste disposal problem. On Oct. 13, the commission issued a task force report[8] that said the environmental consequences were greater than previously believed, but still too small to discontinue licensing. Consequently, on Nov. 5, the NRC ended the moratorium on licensing.

The Natural Resources Defense Council, in a suit filed Sept. 9, asked the U.S. District Court for the District of Columbia to block plans for expanding waste storage facilities at the Hanford Reservation and the Savannah River Plant. The council said ERDA was ignoring a law requiring it to obtain licenses from the Nuclear Regulatory Commission for new tanks. The court was asked to bar construction of 20 tanks until ERDA got a license and filed an environmental impact statement on the project.

An exiled Soviet scientist, Zhores Medvedev, said in London on Nov. 6 that hundreds of Russians were killed and thousands suffered from radiation sickness when buried atomic waste exploded without warning in the Ural Mountains in 1958.

---

[8] "Environmental Survey of the Reprocessing and Waste Management Portions of the LWR Fuel Cycle."

California Gov. Edmund G. Brown Jr. on June 3 signed into law a measure that prohibits the issuance of construction permits for any new nuclear power plants in the state unless the California Energy Commission affirms that the federal government has developed and demonstrated satisfactorily safe techniques for handling nuclear wastes. However, nuclear initiatives that would have imposed similar restrictions in Ohio, Montana, Colorado, Washington, Oregon and Arizona were defeated in the Nov. 2 general election.

Willrich Report on Government Mishandling

Public concern rose further when an official report critical of the government was obtained by a citizens' anti-nuclear group, Critical Mass, and released to the press on Sept. 7. The report, prepared for ERDA by a team of law and engineering students under the direction of Professor Mason Willrich,[9] director of international relations at the Rockefeller Foundation, said the government's past handling of radioactive materials had been "marred in a sufficient number of instances to be a cause for concern." The report cited 18 leaks at the Hanford storage facility, resulting in the loss of over 430,000 gallons of high-level wastes into the surrounding earth. "These leaks have neither killed nor injured anyone to date," Willrich noted. "Nonetheless, their hazard will remain for hundreds of thousands of years."

Willrich found that while there is widespread agreement that nuclear waste must be contained and isolated from the human environment, "controversy surrounds the question of how it will be achieved." He said: "The basic goals of U.S. radioactive waste policy are unclear.... There is today no long-term management of radioactive wastes, no comprehensive scheme for regulation of such waste...." Willrich described present arrangements for handling civilian and military nuclear wastes as "unworkable" because of confusion of roles and unclear regulatory responsibility.

Management of commercial high-level waste [he added] is divided between private industry and the federal government. The private sector is responsible for temporary storage, treatment, packaging, and transport, while the federal government...is responsible for permanent disposition. Bifurcated responsibility for an essentially integrated series of waste management operations creates incentives for each sector to pass [the risks and costs] through to the other as much as possible.... Thus, the existing structure tends to prevent, rather than to facilitate, the efficient management of commercial high-level waste.

[9] Mason Willrich, "Radioactive Waste Management and Regulation," report to the U.S. Energy Research and Development Administration from the MIT Energy Laboratory, Sept. 1, 1976 Draft. At the time of the study Willrich was a visiting professor of nuclear engineering at the Massachusetts Institute of Technology.

To correct the situation he portrayed, Willrich recommended the establishment of a national Radioactive Waste Authority, separate from the Energy Research and Development Administration, to manage all high-level nuclear wastes. ERDA would continue to have primary responsibility for research and development of radioactive waste technology. Willrich also proposed creation of an International Radioactive Waste Commission under the International Atomic Energy Agency in Vienna, Austria.

Options for the Permanent Storage of Wastes

During the past year the federal government has taken a firmer approach toward solving the nuclear waste problem, according to W.D. Rowe, ERDA's top radiation official. "Before it was just a lot of lip service," he said.[10] The agency's budget for fiscal year 1977 showed nearly a sevenfold increase in funding for its commercial waste-management program over the previous year—some $87.5-million, up from $13.5-million. In May, ERDA issued a five-volume report analyzing various technical alternatives for handling and storing commercial radioactive wastes.[11] At present the most favored option is to (1) solidify liquid high-level wastes into glass, ceramics or calcine powder; (2) encapsulate them in cement, concrete or urea-formaldehyde resin; and (3) bury them in stable geologic formations, such as salt beds. This three-step method is attractive because the technology is available and could be put into commercial operation faster than other methods.

The government is studying a large salt formation 30 miles east of Carlsbad, N.M., as a potential site for an experimental waste repository. If tests confirm the area's suitability, construction could begin as early as 1981. ERDA has said that it will have a waste storage project under way by 1985. For at least the first 10 years of operation, the wastes will be buried so that they can be easily dug up and moved to another location if unforeseen problems develop. To handle that contingency—and to assure that no one area can be called the nuclear garbage dump for the entire nation—the government plans to build several more waste storage complexes in other parts of the country. The agency already has begun to look for potential sites in salt, shale and hard-rock formations across the nation.

Salt beds are considered the most likely repositories. The existence of a salt bed indicates that no water has penetrated the

---

[10] Quoted in *The Wall Street Journal*, July 26, 1976.

[11] "Alternatives for Managing Wastes From Reactors and Post-Fission Operations in the LWR Fuel Cycle," ERDA-76-43. The study was undertaken in November 1975 to fulfill a request made by the Joint Congressional Committee for Atomic Energy for a comprehensive analysis of waste management alternatives. The report will be the subject of public review and comment, after which ERDA plans to prepare a draft environmental impact statement on waste management for review in early 1977.

area for a long time; otherwise the salt would have dissolved. This is important because flowing water can carry particles of waste from burial sites into the biosphere. In addition, salt beds are geologically stable; they are not likely to be affected by earthquakes. Finally, salt can mend itself when it is fractured. Consequently, a disposal site in salt would be protected against geologic stress which might cause fissures in other formations. According to H.A. Bethe, "There are roughly 50,000 square miles of salt beds in the United States; only three square miles are needed for disposal of all projected wastes up to the year 2010."

The New Mexico project already has encountered some unexpected problems. The original site had to be abandoned after the drilling exposed a pocket of brine saturated with hydrogen sulfide and methane. Brine indicated the presence of underground water and the gases could pose a safety hazard for workers building or operating the facility. However, ERDA officials say that there is no indication that the brine problem is widespread.

If burial in geologic formations does not prove satisfactory for some reason, there are other possibilities. Since 1974 a consortium of oceanographers and other scientists has been studying the feasibility and cost of burying nuclear wastes beneath the ocean floor. The focus now is on two sites—one in the Pacific about 800 miles northeast of Hawaii and another in the Atlantic about 600 miles northeast of Bermuda. Scientists expect to know by 1985 whether ocean floor burial is feasible. ERDA also is investigating the possibility of creating a very deep underground cavity—possibly with an atomic explosion—and in-

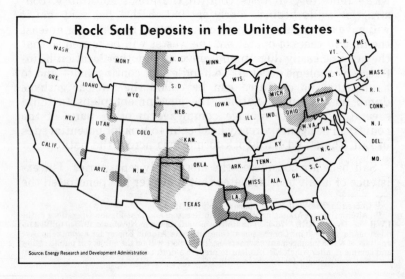

Rock Salt Deposits in the United States

Source: Energy Research and Development Administration

Design for Underground Disposal

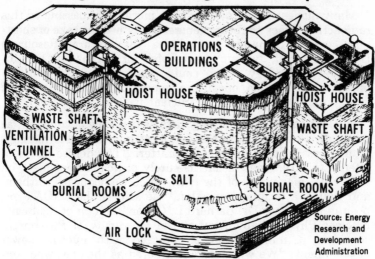

OPERATIONS BUILDINGS

HOIST HOUSE

HOIST HOUSE

WASTE SHAFT

VENTILATION TUNNEL

WASTE SHAFT

SALT

BURIAL ROOMS

BURIAL ROOMS

AIR LOCK

Source: Energy Research and Development Administration

jecting liquid nuclear wastes into it. The theory is that the hot wastes would melt the surrounding underground rocks, which would resolidify so tightly they would contain nuclear wastes.

Another possibility involves a process called transmutation during which long-lived radioactive wastes are bombarded with neutrons inside a reactor to burn off more of the fissionable material, thus shortening their hazardous life. However, the engineering problems are enormous and some radioactive waste products, such as cesium-137 and strontium-90, cannot easily be changed by this bombardment process.

Moral, Ethical Issues in Waste Management

One of the most troubling aspects of the nuclear waste question, according to Daniel Ford, executive director of the Union of Concerned Scientists, "is the fact that it's not just a technical problem that requires some pieces of equipment or some design, but it's a problem that requires human beings to do certain things over a long period of time with a great degree of care and diligence."[12] Similar sentiments were voiced by Jacques Cousteau, the French oceanographer. The containment of nuclear wastes, Cousteau said, "demands that extremely high levels of dedication, vigilance and quality control be maintained without any interruption, indefinitely—a situation totally alien to the human condition. The only way to ensure safety in a nuclear age would be to establish forever a worldwide dictatorship..."[13]

---

[12] Remarks at an American Enterprise Institute Roundtable, in Washington, D.C., May 15, 1975.
[13] Quoted in the *St. Louis Post Dispatch*, Oct. 17, 1976.

Many nuclear critics question the morality of passing on this radioactive legacy to future generations. "For the sake of short-term energy demands," concludes the Natural Resources Defense Council, "we may have opted for a transitory but unforgiving technology which could place a heavy, if not unmanageable, burden on future generations long after safer energy sources have replaced nuclear fission."[14]

Nuclear advocates generally dismiss this type of comment as paranoic. Professor Brooks insists that nuclear waste management is essentially a technical matter. "The degree of moral offense to future generations is surely critically dependent on the actual magnitude of the risks which we bequeath to them, and that is a technical question," he said at the ERDA symposium in Denver. Dr. Bernard L. Cohen, director of the Scaife Nuclear Physics Laboratory at the University of Pittsburgh, considers it immoral not to proceed with nuclear power development: "We will...be remembered as the ones who consumed all the high grade mineral ores and burned up...those once plentiful hydrocarbons—coal, oil and gas.... The only thing that might save us from their [future generations'] curses would be supplying them with a technology that will allow them to live in reasonable comfort without those resources."[15]

Search for Waste Disposal Solution

D URING THE EARLY YEARS of nuclear development, waste management was the stepchild of both the nascent nuclear industry and its parent, the Atomic Energy Commission. Between 1943 and 1955 "priorities were more related to production of nuclear material than waste management," according to a report published by the General Accounting Office, an investigative arm of Congress, on Dec. 18, 1974. Nearly all of the nuclear wastes accumulated during that early period were generated at Hanford, the principal source of plutonium for U.S. nuclear weapons.

To accommodate the large quantities of highly radioactive liquid wastes produced at Hanford, the government built more than 150 underground concrete tanks and lined them with carbon steel. The tanks, holding up to a million gallons each, were buried a few feet below the surface of the ground. Initially the liquid wastes were stored without serious problems. But as

---

[14] *Natural Resources Defense Council Newsletter,* winter 1974-75.
[15] Bernard L. Cohen, "Storing Radioactive Wastes Need Not be a Problem," *Nuclear Engineering International,* October 1976, p. 41.

the system became more complex, the waste became more dangerous and more difficult to confine.[16]

One of the first cautionary notes was found in a classified study of Hanford's ground-water characteristics prepared by the U.S. Geological Survey in 1953.[17] Observing that tank-stored wastes and interconnecting pipelines had occasionally leaked, the report called the tanks a "potential hazard" and concluded that their "true structural life...[is] not entirely known." The first big leak at Hanford occurred in August 1958; about 35,000 gallons of high-level waste seeped into the ground. Fortunately, the clay soil beneath the tank prevented the waste from entering the water table about 200 feet below and eventually draining into the nearby Columbia River.[18]

"[Waste management] is the most important problem facing nuclear power..."

Sen. John O. Pastore (D R.I.),
chairman of the Joint Committee
on Atomic Energy, July 1976

Later that year, 1959, the civilian contractor for Hanford, the Atlantic Richfield Hanford Co., asked the federal government to supply some new tanks. The request was denied because AEC officials said that existing tanks could be made to handle greater amounts by reducing their reserve capacities. Two years later Atlantic Richfield renewed its request, warning that the last empty tank would be filled by 1964. The AEC finally gave in.

But before construction on the new tanks had started, temperature control problems in the old tanks forced the contractor to fill the one remaining tank. Consequently, for two years—from January 1963 until January 1965, when the new tanks were ready for use—no reserve tanks were available for the liquid wastes. This gave rise to what a 1968 report from the General Accounting Office described as "certain operational risks." For example, if one of Hanford's tanks had suddenly developed a sizable leak, it would not have been possible to pump the liquid into a spare tank. But despite the risks, the Hanford reactors were not shut down.

---

[16] Some of the details on the problems at the Hanford Reservation were reported in *The Los Angeles Times,* July 5, 1973.

[17] The study lost its secrecy classification in 1960 but was not made public until 1973.

[18] Information concerning the 1958 leak at Hanford was first published in 1968 in a secret report by the U.S. Comptroller General to the Joint Congressional Committee on Atomic Energy. The report ("Observations Concerning the Management of High-Level Radioactive Waste Material," May 29, 1968) was not declassified until December 1970.

In November 1963 another tank began leaking, but only a small amount of radioactivity was detected. Salt was added to the tank in an effort to seal the leak, and further monitoring convinced the AEC that the leak had been sealed. Despite the leakage that tank was eventually filled even beyond its normal capacity. By December 1964, the tank exceeded its designed capacity by 10 per cent, and during the following months several leaks developed. The GAO commented in its 1968 report:

> From the time the tank was filled in December 1964, until the present [1968], it appears that there has been an increased risk of contaminating the environment with highly radioactive material.
>
> According to the AEC, while facilities have been available for emptying the tank [since 1965], the risks involved in transferring the...materials to other tanks were believed to be much greater than those incurred by allowing the radioactivity to decay in place.

Over the years other leakage problems developed. Between 1958 and 1973 more than 400,000 gallons of high-level waste seeped out of the Hanford tanks. The most serious occurrence was in 1973 when about 115,000 gallons leaked from a 29-year old tank. The leak went undetected from April 20 to June 8. An AEC report attributed the leak partly to aging tanks and primitive monitoring techniques but mainly to managerial laxity and human error on the part of Atlantic Richfield personnel.

So far as could be determined by the commission, no waste came within 100 feet of the local water table, and thus serious consequences were avoided. But Dixy Lee Ray, who was then head of the commission, described the incident as "not only regrettable, but disgraceful."[19] Partly as a result of this accident, the AEC stepped up its efforts to solidify the liquid wastes by evaporating them down to an intensely radioactive "salt cake." However, technical and funding problems have impeded this effort. By 1975, less than half of the high-level wastes stored at Hanford had been solidified.[20]

There have been other waste management problems at Hanford. From the 1950s to the early 1970s, Hanford officials dumped relatively low-level nuclear wastes into concrete-lined, enclosed trenches known as cribs. The cribs were open at the bottom to permit the contaminated liquid to seep down into the soil. The theory was that the soil would absorb plutonium and other radioactive isotopes in much the same way that a water softener traps minerals. Each year more than a million gallons of

---

[19] Quoted in *U.S. News & World Report*, Sept. 10, 1973, p. 32. See also Robert Gillette, "Radiation Spill at Hanford: The Anatomy of an Accident," *Science*, Aug. 24, 1973, pp. 728-730.

[20] See Terry Lash's "Citizen's Guide: The National Debate on the Handling of Radioactive Wastes from Nuclear Power Plants," Natural Resources Defense Council, November 1975, p. 19.

plutonium-contaminated wastes were disposed of in this manner. When the contamination reached a certain level, the dumping was moved to another site.

The agency discovered in 1972 that, despite the precautions, too much plutonium had been allowed to accumulate in one of the cribs. "Due to the quantity of plutonium contained in the soil" beneath the trench, "it is possible to conceive of conditions which could result in a nuclear chain reaction," the commission conceded in a 1972 report. Although the agency tried to minimize the dangers, the threat was enough to convince Congress to appropriate $1.9-million for equipment to enable the AEC to exhume the excess plutonium from the trench.

Additional leakage problems have occurred at the government's two other principal waste storage facilities: the National Reactor Testing Station near Idaho Falls, Idaho, and the Savannah River Plant near Aiken, S.C. The tanks at the Savannah River plant, differing from those at Hanford, have double steel jackets, one inside the concrete and one outside. In theory, if material leaks through the inner lining and through the concrete, it will be trapped by the outer jacket until it can be pumped into another tank. On at least one occasion, however, the amount of leakage exceeded the capacity of the second jacket, and 700 gallons of high-level waste escaped. Some of it entered the local water table. There have been at least six other leaks at the Savannah plant.

Similar problems at the Idaho Falls facility prompted Sen. Frank Church (D Idaho) to ask the AEC to release a National Academy of Sciences' report on waste disposal practices. The report, the product of a study begun in 1955, had been suppressed since it was published in 1966. Under pressure from Senator Church, the commission finally released it on March 7, 1970. The report criticized waste disposal operations at all three disposal sites. It concluded that "considerations of long-range safety are in some instances subordinate to regard for economy of operation." The report also said that "some disposal practices are conditioned on overconfidence in the capacity of the local environment to contain vast quantities of radionuclides for indefinite periods without danger to the biosphere."

Failure of Salt Mine Experiment in Kansas

The release of the National Academy of Sciences' report prompted the Atomic Energy Commission to step up its search for a permanent disposal site. The agency announced plans in 1971 to establish a $25-million National Radioactive Waste Repository in an abandoned salt mine near Lyons, Kan. The commission had been considering the Lyons site since 1955, when it was surveyed by the National Research Council of the

National Academy of Sciences as a possible repository. In March 1971, AEC officials told the Joint Congressional Committee on Atomic Energy that all necessary studies for confirming the Kansas site's suitability had been completed. Milton Shaw, then director of the AEC's Division of Reactor Development, testified that "another year's work of research and development in this area...will not be particularly productive." The final environmental statement on the project asserted: "By establishing this facility, radioactive wastes will be permanently isolated from man's biosphere, thus providing a direct and lasting benefit to the environment."[21]

Some scientists and private citizens were not so confident. The Kansas State Geological Survey argued that the Lyons site had not been adequately tested and said that additional studies were required. One of the more vocal critics of the plan was Rep. Joe Skubitz (R Kan.), who urged state officials to oppose "making Kansas an atomic garbage dump." As it turned out, the plan had to be abandoned after it was discovered that 175,000 gallons of water had mysteriously disappeared from a working salt mine near the proposed waste disposal site.[22]

Criticism of Plan for Interim Surface Storage

After the Kansas plan was shelved, the AEC adopted a new attitude toward waste disposal. In September 1974, the commission issued a draft environmental impact statement[23] which argued that a permanent repository for high-level nuclear waste was not necessary for the next 20 to 100 years. In the meantime, the commission said, the wastes should be placed in interim storage in a specially constructed building known as a Retrievable Surface Storage Facility to be placed on federal land in Washington State, Nevada or Idaho.

Under this plan, the wastes would be stored in 10-foot canisters; about 75,000 might be needed by the year 2000. Because of the intense heat generated by the decaying waste products, the canisters would have to be immersed in water or kept in constantly circulating air. In divulging the plan for interim storage, AEC's director of Waste Management and Transportation, Frank Pittman, emphasized that the plan for permanent disposal of radioactive wastes in bedded salt or some other geologic formation had "in no way been dropped" and was "still a good idea."[24]

---

[21] Atomic Energy Commission, "Radioactive Waste Repository, Lyons, Kansas," WASH-1503, June 1971, p. 2.

[22] See Constance Holden's "Nuclear Waste: Kansans Riled by AEC Plans for Atom Dump," *Science*, April 16, 1971, p. 249, and John Lear's "Radioactive Ashes in the Kansas Salt Cellar," *Saturday Review*, Feb. 19, 1972, p. 39.

[23] Atomic Energy Commission, "Management of Commercial High-Level and Transuranium-Contaminated Radioactive Wastes," WASH-1539, 1974.

[24] Quoted in *Nucleonics Week*, Sept. 19, 1974, p. 10.

Despite Pittman's reassurance, the interim storage plan was widely criticized for ignoring the issue of permanent disposal. The U.S. Environmental Protection Agency gave the AEC impact statement its lowest rating ("inadequate") and said the commission "has reversed the importance of the overall program." The Natural Resources Defense Council said the government should be made to devise a plan for permanent disposal of nuclear wastes before generating additional vast quantities of them.[25] Many critics of the plan feared that interim storage would be prolonged indefinitely.

In September 1975, a National Academy of Sciences panel issued a report saying that retrievable storage was an "acceptable interim stage" for managing high-level wastes if certain precautions were taken. But by that date, the government already had shelved the interim storage plan. The newly created Energy Research and Development Administration[26] had announced the previous April that it was withdrawing its funding request to Congress for the Retrievable Surface Storage Facility.

In a letter to the Joint Congressional Committee on Atomic Energy, ERDA Administrator Robert C. Seamans also said that the agency would replace its September 1974 environmental impact statement with one that would include a "comprehensive reevaluation" of the surface storage idea. As to the future of the Retrievable Surface Storage idea, an ERDA official said in October 1975 that, contrary to some news accounts following the withdrawal of the budget request, "the concept is dormant, but not dead."[27]

Problems at Low-Level Waste Burial Sites

Between 1946 and 1970, the United States dumped 62,000 steel drums containing low-level nuclear wastes into the Atlantic and Pacific Oceans at various places. This practice was gradually discontinued and supplanted by land burial. Today, however, some states are becoming reluctant to accept any more radioactive wastes for land burial. This has prompted the federal government to investigate other options, including a return to ocean dumping.[28] As a first step the Environmental Protection

[25] "Radioactive Wastes: The AEC's Non-Solution," *Natural Resources Defense Council Newsletter,* winter 1974-1975.
[26] The Atomic Energy Commission was formally dissolved in January 1975 and replaced by two agencies, the Energy Research and Development Administration and the Nuclear Regulatory Commission. This separated the dual responsibilities for promoting and regulating nuclear power.
[27] Remarks by Harvey F. Soule, chief of Plans and Evaluation Branch, Nuclear Fuel Cycle and Production Division, at an Atomic Industrial Forum "Workshop on the Nuclear Debate: Basic Issues for 1976," held in Boston on Oct. 28, 1975.
[28] Ocean dumping of low-level nuclear wastes is permitted under the Marine Protection, Research and Surveillance Act of 1972—commonly known as the Ocean Dumping Act. However, it banned the dumping of high-level radioactive wastes into the oceans. Ocean dumping of high-level nuclear wastes also is prohibited by a 1972 international treaty, the Convention on the Prevention of Marine Pollution by Dumping Wastes and Other Matter.

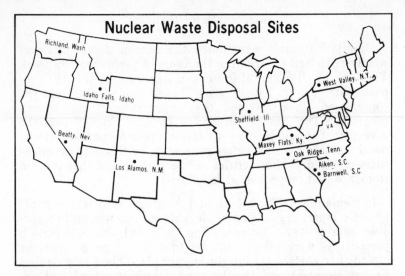

Nuclear Waste Disposal Sites

Agency initiated field studies to determine what had happened to low-level wastes dumped into the oceans in past years.

The findings were not encouraging. Scientists found traces of radioactive cesium leaking from containers at a site 120 miles east of Ocean City, Md. They also found traces of plutonium in ocean sediment off the coast of San Francisco. "Although the presence of these radioactive waste dumpsite contaminants has not been translated into health risks to man or to the environment, it underscores the need to study what happens at dumpsites before ocean dumping of radioactive wastes becomes more widespread," said Environmental Protection Agency oceanographer Robert S. Dyer, in a paper presented to an International Atomic Energy Agency symposium in Vienna last March.

Additional problems have developed with low-level wastes buried on land. Today there are more than 42 million cubic feet of military low-level nuclear waste stored near Richland, Wash.; Idaho Falls, Idaho; Barnwell, S.C.; Oak Ridge, Tenn.; and Los Alamos, N.M. More than nine million cubic feet of commercial low-level waste are stored at other sites near Richland, Wash.; Beatty, Nev.; Sheffield, Ill.; Maxey Flats, Ky.; Barnwell, S.C.; and West Valley, N.Y.[29] In January 1976, the EPA announced that highly toxic plutonium was percolating into the soil from the Maxey Flats burial site. That same month the General Accounting Office reported that radioactivity had oozed from other burial sites at various times.[30]

[29] All of the storage except at Richland is on state-owned land; the Richland site is on federally owned land leased to the state.
[30] "Improvements Needed in the Land Disposal of Radioactive Wastes—A Problem of Centuries," Report to the Congress by the Comptroller General of the United States, RED-76-54, Jan. 12, 1976.

"Although low-level radioactive waste may not represent a significant health hazard at this time," said a report released by the House Government Operations Committee on June 30, 1976, "the performance of existing disposal systems...[has] not been uniformly good and thus, no assurance can be given or conclusion drawn with regard to protection from potential future health hazards." An official from the U.S. Geological Survey told the committee that throughout the 1950s and into the 1960s "more attention was given to the economics of handling the material, and to the cost, location, and ready availability of a site for burial use, than...to the ultimate fate of the waste."

The General Accounting Office report said that some states have not made arrangements—or are receiving inadequate fees from commercial operators—to finance centuries-long care of sites after they are deactivated and become the state's reponsibility, or after an operator is forced out of business. Nor is there adequate provision for financing corrective action, which can be extremely expensive. The GAO suggested that the federal government eventually will be asked to pay the bills. Some persons think that it should assume full control over all the commercial burial sites. The House Government Operations Committee recommended that Congress and the executive branch "give prompt consideration to legislation that would put these sites under the regulatory authority of the Nuclear Regulatory Commission."

Future of Plutonium Reprocessing

PERHAPS THE MOST significant pending decisions concerning nuclear waste management relate to the commercial reprocessing of spent nuclear fuel. Reprocessing is the procedure whereby uranium fuel that has been burned in reactors is turned into a liquid and any remaining uranium and plutonium is separated from useless wastes. The recovered uranium and plutonium can then be recycled—turned into new fuel for use in reactors in the same way it was used originally. "The basic technology," writes Sarah Miller, editor of *Nucleonics Week*, an industry newsletter, "was developed in the weapons program, and the plan was for industry gradually to build up civilian capacity in rhythm with the increase in the number of nuclear reactors."[31]

There are three commercial reprocessing facilities in the United States: the Nuclear Fuel Services plant in West Valley,

[31] Writing in *The New York Times*, Nov. 7, 1976.

N.Y.; General Electric's Midwest Fuel Recovery Plant at Morris, Ill.; and the Allied-General plant in Barnwell, S.C. But all three have been plagued by technical and financial difficulties, and none is operating at this time. The West Valley plant, the only one of the three ever to operate, opened in 1966 but had to close in 1972 for repairs because radioactive leaks were contaminating workers and the environment.

Nuclear Fuel Services, a subsidiary of Getty Oil Co., hoped to reopen the West Valley plant in 1978. After 1972, the plant was enlarged and its management applied for a federal permit to triple its capacity to handle radioactive wastes. But the State of New York, on May 16, 1975, refused to certify the plant, contending that its radioactive discharges would exceed the state's water purity standards. Company officials said early in 1976 that they would not spend the estimated $800-million needed to make the plant safe.

The Energy Research and Development Administration expects the plant to be closed permanently when the Nuclear Fuel Services contract with the state expires in 1980. If that happens, the 600,000 gallons of high-level radioactive wastes stored at the plant will have to be solidified and shipped to a permanent repository. This means that a factory to solidify the wastes will have to be built alongside the reprocessing plant. The cost of building this facility, operating it and shipping the solid wastes will be about $540-million, an independent contractor, Battelle Pacific Northwest Laboratory, told ERDA. The West Valley plant cost $33-million to build 15 years ago, and $17-million has been spent since then in modernizing it.

General Electric's reprocessing plant in Morris, Ill., was scheduled to begin operating in 1974. It was an experimental facility which was trying to simplify and reduce the cost of the recovery process. But the system kept clogging. GE engineers said that repairing or replacing the parts would be extremely difficult and expensive because of high levels of radiation inside the heart of the plant; the company finally decided to abandon the $64-million investment.

Allied General Nuclear Services, a joint subsidiary of Allied Chemical and General Atomic, already has spent $250-million on a reprocessing plant under construction near Barnwell, S.C. To finish the plant and build necessary adjunct facilities, including one to solidify the liquid waste material, is expected to require additional hundreds of millions of dollars. Even if the money were available, Allied General could not start building the needed solidification facility until the Nuclear Regulatory Commission approved a waste solidification technology. Estimates of the plant's opening range from 1978 to 1983.

Allied General's president, A.E. Schubert, proposed to ERDA in 1975 that the federal government complete the plutonium solidification and waste disposal facilities at Barnwell as a "demonstration project." The private concern would buy the government facilities later if the operation became profitable, and in the meantime it would use them for a service fee. Without government support, Schubert implied, the Barnwell plant might have to be mothballed or even dismantled.

Questioning of Necessity for Waste Recycling

The Wall Street Journal and *The Washington Post* reported in October 1976 that the Ford administration was considering a federal bail-out of the Barnwell plant.[32] In a major address on nuclear proliferation delivered on Oct. 28, President Ford did not address the question directly. He said only that he was directing the Energy Research and Development Administration to "begin immediately to define a reprocessing and recycle evaluation program." However, the President went on to say that the United States should "no longer regard the reprocessing of used nuclear fuel to produce plutonium as a necessary and inevitable step in the nuclear fuel cycle." This idea was expanded in a recent article in the *Bulletin of the Atomic Scientists* by Fred C. Iklé, head of the State Department's Arms Control and Disarmament Agency.

> [R]ecycling would not bring independence from imported fuel....[and it] is not guaranteed to save money. But it is guaranteed to accumulate thousands of pounds of plutonium...far more accessible for diversion to weapons manufacture than if it had been left in the spent fuel rods. This plutonium would be distributed throughout the world—enough material for hundreds and hundreds of atomic bombs.... Before we take the plunge into a plutonium fuel economy, let us look very closely at the risks and our ability to control them.[33]

Similar sentiments about the potential dangers of reprocessing and plutonium recycling were expressed by President-elect Carter in his speech at the United Nations on May 13. Carter said the immediate need for plutonium reprocessing "has not yet been demonstrated." To help in preventing the diversion of weapons-grade plutonium from a reprocessing facility, Carter called for a voluntary moratorium on the purchase or sale of reprocessing facilities. Although U.S. policy forbids overseas sales of such plants, several European countries have begun to make such sales. France, for example, has agreed to sell a reprocessing plant to Pakistan, and Brazil has contracted to buy one from West Germany. In May 1974, India detonated a

---

[32] See *The Wall Street Journal*, Oct. 6, 1976, and *The Washington Post*, Oct. 10, 1976.
[33] Fred C. Iklé, "Illusions and Realities about Nuclear Energy," *Bulletin of the Atomic Scientists*, October 1976, pp. 15-16.

nuclear device made from material extracted from a reprocessing plant.[34]

Carter said that if the need for plutonium reprocessing is eventually demonstrated, a centralized multinational reprocessing service should be created under the auspices of the International Atomic Energy Agency. He suggested that the reprocessing plant now under construction at Barnwell, S.C., could become the site of the first multinational reprocessing facility. The Nuclear Regulatory Commission has not yet decided whether to allow the nuclear industry to recycle recovered plutonium and uranium. The agency has said it will decide this question in 1977 after a full-scale review of the economic, environmental and safeguard issues. The commission ruled on Nov. 11, 1975, that in the interim it would consider applications for licenses to operate fuel reprocessing plants and to use plutonium temporarily as a fuel. The NRC ruling was challenged in a court suit filed by the Natural Resources Defense Council and some other environmental groups.

On May 27, 1976, the U.S. Court of Appeals for the Second Circuit (New York) overturned the commission's decision, ruling unanimously that plutonium could not be used as a nuclear fuel on an interim basis before the Nuclear Regulatory Commission completed a study of plutonium's safety and health effects. A lawyer for the Natural Resources Defense Council said the court's decision would mean a minimum delay of several years in the commercial use of plutonium. "This pause," he said, "will give the public and Congress time to consider whether the United States should commit itself, and ultimately the rest of the world, to a plutonium economy...."[35]

Growing Backlog of Spent Fuel Assemblies

Nonetheless, the use of plutonium as a nuclear fuel moved one step closer to reality on Aug. 31, 1976, with the release of a staff report from the Nuclear Regulatory Commission. The report concluded that the health, safety and environmental effects of nuclear power would not change significantly if plutonium were used as a fuel, and that plutonium recycling was economically sound. The report did not cover safeguards needed to protect plutonium from theft and to protect facilities using it from sabotage. These issues will be considered in a separate environmental impact statement expected to be released by the end of the year. Both statements will then serve as the basis for public hearings on the question of whether the United States should go ahead with plutonium reprocessing and recycling.

[34] See "Nuclear Safeguards," *E.R.R.*, 1974 Vol. II, pp. 865-884.
[35] J. Gustave Speth, quoted in *The New York Times*, May 28, 1976.

If the commission does not approve plutonium reprocessing and recycling, then the spent fuel assemblies themselves will have to be disposed of, perhaps buried in one of the geologic formations currently being studied by the government. The spent fuel rods are intensely radioactive and generate tremendous amounts of heat. After removal from the reactor, they are temporarily stored in a large concrete chamber, open at the top and filled with about 40 feet of water. They are positioned in a rigid storage rack at the bottom of the chamber to allow the water to circulate continuously and preclude the possibility of a chain reaction.

The water in the chamber serves two purposes: it acts as a coolant and a radiation shield. A 10-foot cover of water provides as much protection from radioactive rays as a foot of lead or four feet of concrete. Theoretically, these bundles of spent fuel will remain underwater in the cooling tanks for about six months, long enough for some of their radioactive heat to dissipate. Then they can be moved. But in the absence of an operating reprocessing plant or a permanent nuclear waste repository, spent fuel rods have been piling up at nuclear power plants.

The Energy Research and Development Administration has said that at least 18 power reactors may have to shut down by 1978 because of the lack of available storage space.[36] Suggested ways to accommodate the growing backlog include (1) placing the rods closer together in existing storage areas with special measures to prevent a critical mass being formed, (2) shipping spent fuel rods from reactors without sufficient storage space to reactors with unused storage capacity, (3) shipping spent fuel rods to special new storage facilities away from the individual reactors, or (4) shipping spent fuel rods to existing but non-operational reprocessing plants.

According to physicist Marvin Resnikoff, "long-term storage of spent fuel would be less costly than reprocessing."[37] But he goes on to say that there are numerous problems with this approach. One problem centers on the federal government's liquid metal fast-breeder reactor program. The success of this program depends on the recovery of the plutonium produced in the breeder reactor.

Most people assume that the only way to handle nuclear wastes is to store them safely until they lose their radioactivity. But some scientists say there could be alternatives to storage. "It has happened before," Dixy Lee Ray has said, "that today's garbage turns out to be tomorrow's useful product, and this can

---

[36] U.S. Energy Research and Development Administration, "LWR Spent Fuel Disposition Capabilities, 1975-1984," March 1975, ERDA-25.

[37] Marvin Resnikoff, "Expensive Enrichment," *Environment,* July-August 1975, p. 29.

happen with radioactive wastes too, at least to some extent." She noted that various radioisotopes already are being used in industrial processes, in non-destructive testing and in medical research, and that plutonium-run batteries are operating instruments sending back data from the moon. Scientists hope one day to use radioactive cesium to kill germs and viruses in treated sewage sludge, making it safe for use as fertilizers and cattle feed. But many of these developments are far into the future. In the meantime, the government and the nuclear industry must come to grips with the problem of disposing of the increasing amounts of radioactive wastes.

Selected Bibliography

Articles

Cohen, Bernard L., "Storing Radioactive Wastes Need Not Be a Problem," *Nuclear Engineering International,* October 1976.

Cullimore, Don, "Radioactive Wastes Buried by the Bureaucracy," *Environmental Action,* Aug. 28, 1976.

Dau, Gary and Robert Williams, "Secure Storage of Radioactive Waste," *EPRI Journal,* July-August 1976.

Hollocher, Thomas, "Lethal Trash," *Trial,* January-February 1974.

Kulbo, Arthur S. and David J. Rose, "Disposal of Nuclear Wastes," *Science,* Dec. 21, 1973.

Lewis, Richard S., "Radioactive Salt Mine," *Bulletin of the Atomic Scientists,* June 1971.

Resnikoff, Marvin, "Expensive Enrichment," *Environment,* July-August 1975.

Skeptic, July-August 1976 issue.

Studies and Reports

Atomic Industrial Forum, "Background Info" and "Press Info," selected issues.

Editorial Research Reports, "Nuclear Power Options," 1971 Vol. II, p. 585; "Nuclear Safeguards," 1974 Vol. II, p. 865; "Nuclear Safety," 1975 Vol. II, p. 601.

Energy Research and Development Administration, "Alternatives for Managing Wastes From Reactors and Post-Fission Operations in the LWR Fuel Cycle," ERDA-76-43, May 1976.

Federal Energy Resources Council, "Management of Commercial Radioactive Nuclear Wastes: A Status Report," May 10, 1976.

Hayes, Denis, "Nuclear Power: The Fifth Horseman," Worldwatch Paper 6, May 1976.

"Improvements Needed in the Land Disposal of Radioactive Wastes—A Problem of Centuries," report to Congress by the Comptroller General of the United States, Jan. 12, 1976.

"Low-Level Nuclear Waste Disposal," report by the House Government Operations Committee, June 20, 1976.

"Nuclear Power Struggle Hits Critical Stage," Conservation Foundation Newsletter, March-April 1976.

Willrich, Mason, "Radioactive Waste Management and Regulation," report from the MIT Energy Laboratory, Sept. 1, 1976.

Ozone CONTROVERSY

by

John Hamer

Mar. 19
1 9 7 6

OZONE CONTROVERSY

THE OZONE CONTROVERSY burst into public debate in the mid-1970s with confusing and frightening suddenness. Americans were told that their use of aerosol spray cans and air conditioners, among other things, might be endangering the fragile atmospheric ozone layer[1] that protects the earth from solar ultraviolet rays. If the ozone layer were depleted, it was said, the result could be more human skin cancer, damage to plant life, and even global climatic changes. Cries to ban fluorocarbons—the allegedly guilty substances that are used primarily as propellants and refrigerants—were heard throughout the land. And the familiar aerosol spray can was branded as a dangerous weapon that could bring ecological doom.

Before long, however, a catch appeared: it turned out that scientists disagreed as to the seriousness of the hazard. No one really knew how fast the ozone was being depleted, how long it would take before an imminent danger existed, or even if aerosol sprays and other consumer products were indeed the culprits. Findings and conclusions differed, and for every scientist who called for an immediate ban on fluorocarbons there was one who contended that more research was needed before science could be sure. The American public, accustomed to cries of wolf about the environment, shrugged collectively and sat back to await the verdict.

Today, the jury is still out on the ozone controversy. In April, a special panel of the National Academy of Sciences is scheduled to release a comprehensive report on the ozone question, the result of more than a year of study. But the chances are slim that it will resolve the debate completely. For if there is one thing on which the majority of scientists now seem to agree, it is that a final, definitive answer on the relationship of fluorocarbons to the ozone layer is still many years away. Too little is known—about the atmosphere and the climate, about the effects of ultraviolet light on plant and animal life, and about the comparative concentrations of man-made and natural chemicals in

[1] The earth's atmosphere is divided into several layers: the troposphere (0-10 miles high), the stratosphere (10-35 miles), the mesosphere (35-50 miles), the thermosphere (50-300 miles) and the exosphere (300 miles and beyond). The ozone layer is concentrated in the stratosphere.

the atmosphere—to say for certain what the facts are. It is at least possible that the potential danger is exaggerated and that fluorocarbons will turn out to be relatively harmless when all the evidence is in.

But it is also possible that the initial theories were correct, and that fluorocarbons are a serious threat to the atmospheric ozone layer and to all life on earth. If this proves true, the consequences for humanity could be enormous in severity and scope. What complicates the situation is that the effects of fluorocarbons on the ozone layer are delayed—those released at ground level today will not reach the stratosphere for several years. So if fluorocarbon production continues at its present rate, and the ozone-depletion theory is correct, then damage to the ozone layer will continue well into the next century. This is what makes the ozone controversy so critical—the stakes are high, and they involve the entire world, not just the nation.

Widespread Use of Fluorocarbons by Industry

Complicating the issue still further is the fact that fluorocarbons are used in more than $8-billion worth of products manufactured every year in the United States, including about $5.5-billion worth of refrigeration and air conditioning systems and $2-billion worth of aerosols. Fluorocarbon producers and related manufacturing industries employ more than 200,000 workers, with an annual payroll of about $4.5-billion.[2] The six U.S. producers of fluorocarbons *(see below)* employ about 4,000 workers at 14 plants around the country, according to a federal interagency task force *(see box, p. 51)*.

Company	Plant Capacity *(in pounds)*	Trade Name
E.I. du Pont de Nemours & Company	500,000,000	Freon
Allied Chemical Corp.	310,000,000	Genetron
Union Carbide Corp.	200,000,000	UCON
Pennwalt Chemical Corp.	115,000,000	Isotron
Kaiser Aluminum and Chemical Corp.	50,000,000	Kaiser
Racon, Inc.	20,000,000	Raycon

Restrictions on the use of fluorocarbons would have a significant economic impact nationwide, and the affected industries argue strongly that any restrictions should be imposed gradually rather than immediately.

U.S. fluorocarbon manufacturers have pledged, however, to stop making the substances if a clear and imminent hazard is

---

[2] Dana L. Thomas, "The Sky Is Falling!" *Barron's*, March 3, 1975, p. 2.

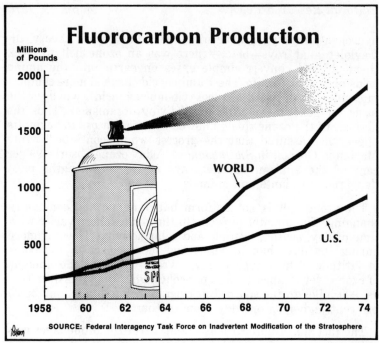

Fluorocarbon Production

Millions of Pounds

SOURCE: Federal Interagency Task Force on Inadvertent Modification of the Stratosphere

proved conclusively. Tom Alexander wrote in *Fortune* magazine, "Fortunately, in an era that seems to equate precipitate action with virtue, science, government, and industry on the whole have handled the ozone issue with a refreshing maturity and tentativeness."[3] Even so, only 50 per cent of the world's fluorocarbons are made in the United States, and the world's other manufacturers may or may not follow the American example. Other countries seem to be waiting for the U.S. lead, but it is uncertain what they will do. To be truly effective, a ban would have to be imposed and enforced worldwide.

Theoretical Threat of Fluorocarbons to Ozone

The focus of all this concern, the ozone layer, is a thin belt in the stratosphere about 10 to 20 miles above the earth's surface. Ozone, a bluish gas that is a toxic pollutant on earth *(see box, p. 57),* is a form of oxygen whose molecules consist of three atoms instead of two. It is highly unstable, ready to give up its extra atom at almost any time. There is about 100 times as much ozone in the upper atmosphere as there is on earth, but even if the ozone layer were on the earth's surface under sea-level temperature and pressure, it would measure only about a tenth of an inch thick.

Ozone was formed millions of years ago when water vapor rose into the atmosphere and was broken up by sunlight into

---

[3] "What We Know—And Do Not Know—About the Ozone Shield," *Fortune,* August 1975.

49

hydrogen and oxygen molecules. According to one theory, ultraviolet solar rays—before there was an ozone belt to block them—helped convert simple gases on earth into the amino acids necessary for life. These amino acids formed more complex molecules, such as DNA (deoxyribonucleic acid), which is the basis for genetic evolution in all living organisms. "Thus the absence of the ozone shield allowed the life process to begin; its appearance assured that the process would continue," wrote Marianna Gosnell in *Smithsonian.*[4] Today ozone absorbs 99 per cent of the sun's ultraviolet rays at the wavelengths most dangerous to plants and animals.

The ozone belt is not uniform but dynamic and constantly changing. The amount of ozone in the stratosphere varies with time of day, season, latitude and solar activity. There is more during the day than at night and more closer to the poles in latitude. "On a typical day," wrote Gosnell, "the amount of ozone over Minnesota is 30 per cent higher than it is over Texas, 900 miles to the south. But even in Minnesota it may be 25 per cent higher on one day than another."

The fact that fluorocarbons might affect the ozone layer was not even suspected until 1974, when two University of California chemists began an academic investigation of what happens to fluorocarbons in the atmosphere *(see p. 56)*. The two fluorocarbons of principal concern are known as F-11 and F-12, which are used primarily as propellants. Fluorocarbons are the propellant in about 50 to 60 per cent of all aerosol products, and they constitute more than 90 per cent of all refrigerants. They are desirable for these purposes because of their unique qualities: they are inert, odorless, nonflammable and insoluble in water. They are chemically stable, which means they do not react or combine with other chemicals or the contents of cans in which they are propellants.

But although they are chemically inert in the lower atmosphere, eventually fluorocarbons are lifted into the stratosphere by wind circulation and diffusion. Here, according to scientific theories, strong sunlight—specifically ultraviolet radiation—decomposes them and releases free chlorine atoms. The chlorine atoms (Cl) act as catalysts, combining with ozone (O_3) to form oxygen (O_2) and chlorine oxide (ClO), which then reacts with another oxygen molecule to form more oxygen and release the chlorine, as follows:

$$Cl + O_3 \rightarrow ClO + O_2$$
$$ClO + O \rightarrow Cl + O_2$$

[4] Marianna Gosnell, "Ozone—The Trick Is Containing It Where We Need It," *Smithsonian,* June 1975, p. 51.

IMOS Report

The Interagency Task Force on Inadvertent Modification of the Stratosphere (IMOS), representing 15 federal departments and agencies, released its final report in June 1975. It concluded that the release of man-made fluorocarbons into the atmosphere was "a legitimate cause for concern," and "unless new scientific evidence is found to remove the cause for concern," it would be necessary to restrict uses of F-11 and F-12 to replacement of fluids in existing refrigeration and air conditioning equipment and to closed systems not involving release into the atmosphere.

Recognizing that the National Academy of Sciences was conducting its own study, the report said, "If the NAS confirms the current...assessment, the task force recommends that the federal regulatory agencies initiate rulemaking procedures for implementing regulations to restrict fluorocarbon uses."

Such restrictions "could reasonably be effective" by January 1978, the IMOS report said. It said that scientific studies during the 1974-75 period altered the quantitative predictions for future ozone depletion, but none cast doubt on the basic theory.

The net result of the chain reaction is that ozone is decreased; one chlorine atom is believed capable of destroying thousands of ozone molecules. Chlorine atoms are considered to be about six times more powerful in destroying ozone than nitrogen oxides, which set off a similar chain reaction.

It is difficult to tell how much man-made fluorocarbons have depleted the ozone layer, however. For one thing, the ozone layer varies naturally so much that many scientists believe a 5 to 10 per cent decrease in atmospheric ozone would have to be observed over several years to prove that human activity was responsible. From 1955 to 1970, total ozone levels in the northern hemisphere apparently increased by about 5 to 10 per cent, according to the federal Interagency Task Force on Inadvertent Modification of the Stratosphere (IMOS, *see above*). Since 1970, atmospheric ozone has declined by about 1 to 2 per cent; natural variations, including sunspot activity, are thought to be responsible.

When the IMOS report was issued in June 1975, various calculations indicated that fluorocarbon production and release may have reduced the ozone layer by 0.5 to 1 per cent, and possibly by as much as 2 per cent. Fluorocarbons already released but not yet ascended to the stratosphere would eventually cause a 1.3 to 3 per cent reduction in the ozone layer even if no other fluorocarbons were released, the report said. And if fluorocarbon release continued at the 1972 rate, the reduction would amount to 7 per cent after several decades.

51

The only findings that might change its conclusions significantly, the report said, would be: (1) the discovery of large natural sources of chlorine in the stratosphere that would make the addition of man-made fluorocarbons insignificant, or (2) the identification of major "sinks" for chlorine on earth which might absorb chlorine before it had a chance to affect the ozone layer. Even so, unforeseen sinks "could decrease, but probably not eliminate, the predicted ozone reduction," the report said.

Link Between Ozone Depletion and Skin Cancer

While no one knows for sure what would happen if the ozone layer were significantly depleted, science provides some clues. Stratospheric ozone screens out most of a middle-wavelength band of solar ultraviolet light known as "ultraviolet-B." It is generally acknowledged that each 1 per cent reduction in ozone concentrations at the earth's middle latitudes, by whatever cause, means about a 2 per cent increase in ultraviolet-B radiation at the earth's surface. The major fear is that increased ultraviolet-B, generally regarded as most harmful to living tissues, would cause a rise in human skin cancer and damage other animal, plant and marine life.

The connection between ultraviolet radiation and some forms of skin cancer is well established. Among white persons in the United States, the annual incidence of skin cancer is about 150 cases per 100,000 population; there are more than 300,000 cases nationwide every year. Most skin cancer occurs on exposed parts of the body, such as the hands, neck or face, and the incidence roughly doubles with every 10 degrees of latitude toward the equator as the ozone layer gets thinner.

It is widely believed that a 1 per cent decrease in the ozone layer will produce about a 2 per cent rise in skin cancer cases. Skin cancer can be treated and is seldom fatal, although there are about 8,000 cases per year of the dreaded melanoma, a form of skin cancer that is often fatal. Melanoma is not known to be caused by ultraviolet radiation, even though there is strong suspicion of a link. Increased ultraviolet radiation also can cause severe sunburn, eye damage and possible changes in Vitamin D balance in some individuals. And there is evidence that it might have a detrimental effect on livestock and wildlife.

Dr. Frederick Urbach, chairman of the department of dermatology at Temple University Medical School in Philadelphia, told the Senate Subcommittee on the Upper Atmosphere at hearings March 1, 1976, that there were many unknowns about the effects of increased ultraviolet radiation on humans. "We need many more studies. We need better epidemiology. The kinds of studies that would be helpful simply have not been done," Urbach said.

The potential impact on plant and marine life is fairly speculative since relatively little research has been done. Donald T. Krizek, a research plant physiologist with the U.S. Department of Agriculture and chairman of a special IMOS subcommittee on biological and climatic effects research, told the Senate subcommittee that "the potential ramifications for agricultural production and the natural environment may...be significant," but that more research was needed. There also has been speculation that ultraviolet rays can penetrate the ocean surface and destroy plankton, thus disrupting the entire marine ecosystem. But Dr. Edward S. Epstein, associate administrator for environmental monitoring and prediction at the National Oceanic and Atmospheric Administration, said there is yet no instrument accurate enough to measure the rays' penetration of sea water.

As for climatic effects, there has been speculation that a thinning of the ozone layer could mean temperature and wind changes in the stratosphere since ozone acts as a heat source by absorbing ultraviolet, as well as infrared and visible, radiation. Such shifts in the stratosphere might lead to changes in growing seasons, the location of deserts and rain belts and even the levels of the oceans. Robert E. Dickinson, leader of a climate research project at the National Center for Atmospheric Research in Boulder, Colo., told the subcommittee that possible human-caused changes in the ozone layer could change global mean temperatures by a few tenths of a degree Centigrade; a 1ºC change would be regarded as a major shift in climate.[5]

Origins of the Fluorocarbon Debate

THE FLUOROCARBON INDUSTRY got its start in 1928, when a General Motors research director and a Frigidaire chief engineer (Frigidaire then was a division of GM) decided that the refrigeration industry needed a new refrigerant if it was to progress. Refrigeration then was based on such materials as ammonia, carbon dixoide and hydrocarbons, all of which had drawbacks. Thomas Midgley Jr., a GM chemist who had discovered earlier that tetraethyl lead was an effective anti-knock gasoline additive, tried using various fluorine compounds as refrigerants. Fluorocarbons worked. They were nonflammable, had low toxicity and low reactivity.

"By October 1929, the Frigidaire Division...had a small experimental plant in operation, and less than a year later Kinetic

[5] See "World Weather Trends," *E.R.R.*, 1974 Vol. II, pp. 515-537.

Some Typical Aerosol Products

	Per Cent of Propellant	Per Cent of Product Concentrate
Feminine hygiene spray	95	5
Anti-perspirant	90	10
Underarm deodorant	90	10
Insect repellant	70	30
Anti-fogging agents	60	40
Floor wax	50	50
Frying pan spray	45	55
Varnish	41	59
Pre-laundry spot remover	30	70
White enamel	27	73
Oven cleaner	25	75

SOURCE: Students Resisting Aerosol Fluorocarbon Emissions

Chemicals was founded to manufacture and sell the new refrigerant," wrote Martin Sherwood, science policy editor of *New Scientist* magazine, in a recent article recounting the industry's history.[6] "This company, owned 51 per cent by DuPont and 49 per cent by GM, registered the Freon trademark in 1931."

In the 1940s the value of fluorocarbons as aerosol propellants was recognized. Aerosols themselves were not new. As early as 1899, patents had been granted on aerosols using methyl and ethyl chloride as propellants, and some products were marketed in the early 1900s. The first use of fluorocarbons as propellants apparently came during World War II, when they were used in insecticide "bug bomb" sprays. Although these were housed in heavy, expensive steel containers, some 4.5 million cans were sold to the public in 1947.

The first "personal" consumer aerosol product was a hair spray in 1950. That year 30 million aerosol containers were sold in the United States—seven times more than in 1947. But in the early 1950s an event occurred which was to revolutionize the aerosol industry. Robert H. Abplanalp, later to become known for his friendship to President Nixon, invented a low-cost, no-leak plastic valve that allowed the contents of an aerosol can to be mixed with the propellant gas smoothly and efficiently. Abplanalp's privately held Precision Valve Corp. secured an unchallenged position in the spray valve market. In 1954, annual production of aerosols reached 188 million cans; by 1958, production passed the 500 million mark; and in 1968, 2.3 billion aerosols were sold.

[6] Reprinted in *Atlas World Press Review*, December 1975, p. 11.

"By 1970, practically every product that was conceivably sprayable either had been packaged or was being considered for packaging in aerosol form," wrote Paul Brodeur in *The New Yorker.*[7] "As a result, more than three hundred different uses have been devised for aerosols, which dispense everything from baby powder, slip preventive for bathtubs, breath sweeteners, and cheesespreads to cooking-pan coatings, nasal sprays, oven cleaners, rug shampoo, shoe polish, telephone disinfectant, waxes, weed killers, and whipped-cream substitutes."

Today, aerosol sales and marketing represent a $3-billion annual business in the United States, with personal products such as hair sprays, deodorants and shaving cream accounting for 50 per cent of the sales. In 1973, nearly three billion aerosols were made and sold—about 14 for every U.S. citizen. "Small wonder that the average American family is estimated to possess between 40 and 50 cans of aerosol in various parts of the house," Brodeur wrote. U.S. fluorocarbon usage, about half of which goes into aerosol propellants, is estimated to be about half of total world usage.

First Discovery of Ozone Layer's Vulnerability

The first suggestion that human activities could affect the stratospheric ozone layer came in 1970, when meteorologist Paul Crutzen, then of the University of Stockholm but on leave at Oxford University, theorized that nitrogen compounds released from decaying plant life on earth could reach the stratosphere and react with ozone to break down ozone molecules. Natural sources of nitrogen were not thought to do much damage, but man-made sources—such as nitrogen fertilizers and nuclear explosions—could seriously affect the ozone layer, according to Crutzen's theory.

About the same time, the nationwide fight over the controversial supersonic transport (SST) plane was coming to a head. James McDonald, an atmospheric physicist at the University of Arizona and a strong opponent of the SST, charged that water vapor in the airplane's exhaust fumes also could deplete the ozone layer. McDonald was among the first to link ozone depletion with the possibility of damage to plant and animal life. Although his theory was highly speculative, it found many adherents among environmentalists and other opponents of the supersonic transport.

Harold Johnston, a chemist at the University of California at Berkeley, examined the exhaust question and, along with Crutzen, found that it was not so much water vapor as nitrogen compound emissions, such as nitric oxides, that could harm the

---

[7] "Annals of Chemistry—Inert," *The New Yorker*, April 7, 1975, p. 47.

ozone layer. This argument influenced the 1971 decision by Congress not to provide further public financing of a supersonic transport then being developed by Boeing. Moreover, it led the Department of Transportation to undertake a $60-million, three-year study called the "Climatic Impact Assessment Program" to determine if a fleet of these planes really could destroy the ozone layer.

This study, which has been described as "perhaps the most expensive after-the-fact technological assessment ever produced in the U.S.,"[8] concluded that 500 such planes built along the Boeing design could cause a 20 per cent reduction of ozone and let 40 per cent more ultraviolet radiation fall on the earth's surface. However, the study found that a fleet of 175 planes operating four and a half hours daily, would reduce the ozone layer by only 1.2 per cent—perhaps serious in the long run but not much different for the individual than a move from Washington, D.C., to Atlanta. The report also said that improved engines and fuels would decrease the danger.

The next step in the ozone controversy was attributable to James Lovelock, an independent British chemist and philosopher who in the 1950s had invented an exquisitely sensitive instrument known as the "electron capture-detector gas chromatograph." It was accurate enough to detect atmospheric gases in concentrations as minute as one part per trillion, whereas previous instruments were able to detect only one part per million. In 1970 Lovelock had discovered that traces of two man-made compounds, trichlorofluoromethane and dichlorofluoromethane, commonly known as F-11 and F-12, were widely dispersed throughout the atmosphere. Lovelock traced the compounds all over the world and found about 30 parts per trillion even in air samples taken from shipboard in the North and South Atlantic. His main interest, however, was tracing air movement and wind direction for climatic studies, so he regarded the inert gases as potentially valuable tools rather than possibly dangerous substances.

Connection of Fluorocarbons to Ozone Depletion

"The assumption that chlorofluorocarbons would be innocuous in the environment because they were chemically inert might have gone unchallenged for some time," wrote Paul Brodeur in *The New Yorker*. But at a scientific conference in Florida, someone mentioned their curious persistence to F. Sherwood Rowland, a chemist at the University of California at Irvine, who began to wonder what ultimately became of the man-made compounds. In the summer of 1973, Rowland got a

---

[8] By Lee Edson in "Not With a Bang But a Pfffft?" *The New York Times Magazine*, Dec. 21, 1975, p. 38.

Ozone on Earth

The ozone layer in the stratosphere is vital to life on earth, but at ground level ozone is considered a toxic pollutant. The word ozone comes from the Greek, meaning "to smell." The odor of ozone is detectable near toy electric trains, leaky power lines and lightning. It is created when a spark passes through dry air and splits oxygen molecules (O_2) into free oxygen atoms which then merge with other oxygen molecules to form ozone (O_3).

For years ozone was used as a disinfectant, bleach or deodorizer, but in the 1940s it was discovered that ozone was damaging tires and other rubber products in the Los Angeles area. Scientists learned that ozone was an ingredient created in smog, and also was harming flowers, vegetables, trees and humans. A lung irritant, it can cause coughing, fatigue and pain, especially in infants, the elderly and the ill.

Nature is another source of ozone, however. Evergreen trees and some other plants emit hydrocarbons known as terpenes, which react with sunshine and nitrogen oxides in the air to form ozone. About 55,000 tons of terpenes are released every day, more than half as much as automobile pollutants. The ozone they create, together with ozone descending from the upper atmosphere and ozone from man-made sources, is especially damaging during spring and summer growing seasons.

research grant from the Atomic Energy Commission to study the question, and that fall he and his associate, Mario J. Molina, a Mexican photochemist, set out to prove that fluorocarbons were not indestructible.

"It began as a typical academic study," Rowland later recalled.[9] "We were trying to figure out something of no possible interest to anyone but other scientists." Rowland and Molina hypothesized that the inert fluorocarbons must be floating unchanged to the stratosphere, where strong ultraviolet rays in sunlight would cause them to release chlorine atoms. These atoms would act as catalysts to destroy ozone, with each chlorine atom capable of setting off a chain reaction involving thousands of ozone molecules. "I kept saying to myself, 'This looks big,' but I hadn't read anything about it, so I figured there must be some flaw," Rowland recalled.

After checking and rechecking their calculations, Rowland and Molina were unable to find any errors. They concluded that a 20 to 40 per cent reduction of the ozone layer was possible even though the depletion would be less if production of the compounds ceased immediately. The most disturbing conclusion was that the full effect of fluorocarbons already in the at-

[9] Quoted by Michael Drosnin in "Not With a Bang, But With a Pssssst!" *New Times*, March 7, 1975, p. 28.

mosphere would not be felt for at least a decade, since the gases floated up and down until they gradually ascended to the ozone layer. "There was no moment of Eureka! really," Rowland recalled. "I just came home one night and told my wife, 'The work is going very well, but it looks like the end of the world.' "[10]

Rowland and Molina paid a visit to Harold Johnston at Berkeley, the scientist who had investigated the SST's effects on the ozone layer. Johnston not only confirmed their findings but told them of three previous experiments which also had revealed chlorine as having a destructive impact on the ozone layer. These findings had not been published because no one was aware of any potential source of chlorine in the upper atmosphere. In January 1974, Rowland wrote an article about their findings and sent it to the British scientific journal *Nature*, which published it in June.

But the Rowland-Molina theory did not make news until September, when they spoke to the American Chemical Society meeting in Atlantic City, N.J. By then, the two scientists had calculated that if fluorocarbon production continued to increase at the present rate of 10 per cent annually until 1990, about 5 to 7 per cent of the ozone layer would be destroyed by 1995 and between 30 and 50 per cent would be gone by the year 2050. They warned that such a depletion could increase skin cancer, cause genetic mutations or crop damage, and might shift world weather patterns. Finally, Rowland and Molina argued that the use of fluorocarbons as aerosol propellants and refrigerants was not worth the risk involved, and urged that they be banned.

Much of the resulting publicity was sensational and alarmist. It also generated a spate of similar studies and calculations aimed at confirming or disproving the ozone-depletion theory. One early report, by Paul Crutzen, then with the National Center for Atmospheric Research in Boulder, Colo., essentially confirmed the Rowland-Molina study. Two investigations by Climatic Impact Assessment Program research teams—one led by Ralph Cicerone of the University of Michigan's Space Physics Research Laboratory and the other by Michael McElroy of Harvard University's Center for Earth and Planetary Physics—also confirmed the depletion theory.

Subsequent Studies That Disputed Earlier Findings

As more studies were conducted, however, doubts arose about the original Rowland-Molina timetable and findings. Douglas Davis, a chemist at the University of Maryland, found that the chlorine-ozone reaction in the stratosphere occurred more slowly than first was thought. Davis found that chlorine reacted with methane to form hydrochloric acid, which fell to earth as

---

[10] Quoted by Drosnin, *op. cit.*, p. 28.

rain. This reduced the amount of chlorine reacting with ozone, Davis found, and cut by 50 to 65 per cent the predicted ozone destruction rate.

Another study, by Pierre Ausloos and Richard Robbert of the National Bureau of Standards, found that stratospheric temperature variations—which had not been considered fully in previous experiments, made the ozone breakdown occur more slowly than was previously assumed. Another experiment, by Michael McElroy and Steven Wofsy of Harvard University, led them to predict that if fluorocarbon production continued at the 1974 rate, the ozone level would decrease by only 7 per cent by the year 2100. And Crutzen, in a revised prediction, said that if world propellant production stopped in 1978 the maximum effect would be an ozone-layer depletion of 1.7 per cent by 1988, or a 1.2 per cent depletion if propellant production stopped in 1975.[11] This difference of 0.5 per cent has been used widely to support the argument that another two or three years of research could be undertaken without any severe risk.

Another contention by scientists disputing earlier findings has been that we simply do not understand enough about the atmosphere or the ozone layer to make accurate predictions as to what will happen under various fluorocarbon-production scenarios. They point out that the atmosphere may remove chlorine or restore ozone on its own. In 1968, for example, after an atmospheric nuclear test in China, ozone over Japan increased 20 per cent instead of decreased as expected. "Air is not static. It is dynamic," James Angell of the National Oceanic and Atmospheric Administration has said.[12] "It may be that normal cyclical forces are at work to replace ozone at the same rate it is lost and thus balance what man destroys. Other forces, such as sunspots, may also be at work. These forces may be more powerful than we realize."

Some scientists have been seeking other sources of stratospheric chlorine, and have found that such compounds as carbon tetrachloride, methyl chloride and methyl chloroform may outweigh fluorocarbons in the atmosphere by far. Methyl chloride, formed during the evaporation of sea water, might be part of a natural balancing system. The implication is that nature may have a method of removing chlorine from the atmosphere before it can do much damage. Other scientists are investigating man-made sources, and have found that methyl bromide, used as a soil fumigant, and the chlorine compounds used in water purification and paper manufacturing may be

---

[11] *See* Tom Alexander, "What We Know—And Do Not Know— About the Ozone Shield," *Fortune,* August 1975.

[12] Quoted by Lee Edson, p. 45.

significant sources of stratospheric chlorine. As yet, no one really knows how much the ozone layer is endangered by human activity or how much earth's natural systems may be relied upon to correct matters.

Research Needs and Legal Action

THE MANY UNKNOWNS about the ozone-fluorocarbon connection have led many scientists, industry spokesmen and government officials to call for further research before a final decision is made on the issue. At the same time, other scientists, officials and environmentalists insist that the risks of waiting outweigh the dangers of an immediate ban on fluorocarbons. A consensus seems to be developing, however, that if the National Academy of Sciences study essentially confirms the conclusions of the IMOS task force report, then restrictions on the use of fluorocarbons should be put in effect by January 1978.

H. Guyford Stever, chairman of the Federal Council for Science and Technology, told the Senate Upper Atmosphere Subcommittee March 1, 1976, that this was "a pretty good timetable.... Aiming for a time when we will get quite serious about it is a good idea." However, Stever acknowledged that the decision would have to be made on the basis of incomplete information. "It is not possible to obtain a complete understanding of the total environmental effects of ozone reduction within the next two years, or probably even within the next 10 years."[13]

In November 1975, a special IMOS subcommittee on biological and climatic effects was formed to assess research needs. Its recent draft report, "A Proposed Federal Research Program to Determine the Biological and Climatic Effects of Stratospheric Ozone Reduction," lists several matters which should receive priority attention during the next two years. They include:

Instrumentation Needs. Developing better equipment for measuring and simulating ultraviolet radiation of various wavelengths.

Human Health Effects. Studying the epidemiology of non-melanoma skin cancer.

Molecular and Cellular Effects. Investigating the damage and repair mechanisms of cells and molecules to determine if ultraviolet radiation might produce genetic effects.

Effects on Plants. Determining the potential impact on native and crop plants at the organism, as well as the ecosystem, level.

---

[13] See "Pollution Control: Costs and Benefits," *E.R.R.*, 1976 Vol. I, pp. 145-164.

The report also recommended a long-term research program to study: direct effects of increased ultraviolet rays on natural, agricultural and managed forest ecosystems; direct effects of climate changes; and indirect effects of climate changes on ecosystems. The Environmental Protection Agency is coordinating the federal research efforts.

In addition to federally sponsored research, the fluorocarbon manufacturers are backing a research program under the auspices of the Manufacturing Chemists Association, a trade organization. It is sponsoring research at various universities that is expected to cost $3-million to $5-million. Ray McCarthy, research director of DuPont, has said: "I hope that the measurements now planned and under way will prove effective in *unequivocally* providing information on the reaction of chlorine in the stratosphere. If not, we will seek other methods which will give us that unequivocal proof."[14] The problem is that the definitiion of unequivocal is subjective.

Another aspect of the debate over how much research is sufficient involves the delicate matter of scientific "grantsmanship." Sean Mitchell raised this question in an article in *The Nation:* "The whole area of research grants and the competition among scientists to get them must be considered a factor in the politics of ozone. Atmospheric science is a field not widely developed; there is a lot yet to be learned about the stratosphere, and many scientists would like to use whatever leverage they can to get a commitment from the government for long-range research in the area. Aside from concern about the environment, there are careers to be made."[15]

At the Senate subcommittee hearings, there was much discussion of a proposal to create "centers of excellence" to coordinate experimental studies and results on the ozone issue. But Dr. Edward S. Epstein of the National Oceanic and Atmospheric Administration observed: "I think there is a real problem that 'centers of excellence' might be more concerned with promoting excellence at their own centers than in coordinating a larger body of information and research." Whatever the form and whoever the sponsors, a great number of research studies are now under way to seek answers on ozone.

Outlook for Ban, Restrictions or Alternatives

There is considerable effort at the state and local levels to ban fluorocarbons before federal and industry research is completed. The Oregon legislature passed a law to forbid the sale of fluorocarbons beginning in 1977, and at least 10 other states

---

[14] Quoted by Janet H. Weinberg, "Ozone Verdict: On Faith or Fact?" *Science News,* May 17, 1975, p. 324.

[15] "The Politics of Ozone," *The Nation,* June 28, 1975, p. 777.

have similar bills pending. There are numerous lawsuits by citizen and public-interest groups to restrict the use of fluorocarbons, although none has succeeded as yet and the appeals process is expected to drag them out for several years. There are bills before Congress to ban or control fluorocarbons, although final action on any of them is unlikely before the National Academy of Sciences issues its final report. The fluorocarbon issue also is a part of the continuing controversy over the Concorde, the supersonic passenger plane manufactured by Britain and France.

In response to such sentiment, the fluorocarbon industry and the manufacturers of products that rely on fluorocarbons are investigating—and in some cases already selling—alternatives to the controversial compounds. The makers of several hair sprays, deodorants and waxes have been advertising non-aerosol versions of their products, and have reported brisk sales of these alternatives. However, most industry observers regard this as a marketing ploy rather than a comprehensive commitment to phasing out fluorocarbon products. Even so, there is a possibility that consumer response will bring about a changeover in the marketplace. Shipments of aerosol spray cans in the United States were down about 25 per cent in the first half of 1975 as compared to a similar period in 1974.[16]

In addition to economic considerations of restricting or banning fluorocarbons, questions of household safety have been raised.[17] "More babies and young children might die from ingesting common household substances such as medicines, pesticides and cleaning agents," Tom Alexander wrote in *Fortune*. "Tests indicate that it is much easier to swallow the contents of a bottle than those of an aerosol can and, in fact, that babies are repelled by the chilling spray."

Still, the aerosol spray problem is considered minor compared to the refrigeration issue. Mechanical refrigeration systems that use fluorocarbons as the coolant predominate; they include household refrigerators, fresh meat and vegetable storage systems, home and automobile air conditioners, commercial and residential freezers, building air conditioners, and transportation cold-storage systems. "Given the heavy dependence of virtually every link of the food chain upon refrigeration, an immediate ban on their use would be a recipe for mass food spoilage, shortages, price increases, and wrenching economic dislocations," Alexander wrote. Even if a suitable substitute

---

[16] "The Ozone-Layer Controversy," *Atlas World Press Review*, December 1975, p. 12.

[17] R. E. Shamel, J. K. O'Neill and R. Williams, "Preliminary Economic Impact Assessment of Possible Regulatory Action to Control Atmospheric Emissions of Selected Halocarbons," Arthur D. Little, Inc., prepared for the Environmental Protection Agency, September 1975, p. I-4.

World Use of Fluorocarbons, 1973

Use	Amount (in pounds)	Per Cent
Aerosol Propellants	1,310,000,000	55
Refrigerants	695,000,000	29
Foam blowing agents	165,000,000	7
Solvents	100,000,000	4
Plastics and resins	65,000,000	3
Other	45,000,000	2
Total	2,380,000,000	100

SOURCE: Arthur D. Little, Inc.

refrigerant were found and introduced into new refrigeration systems nationwide, there still would be some release of fluorocarbons into the atmosphere from systems which had not been converted or old systems which had been discarded.

"A primary concern in any discussion of fluorocarbon regulation is the hard fact that at present there are no viable alternatives for fluorocarbons for manufacturers of refrigeration and air conditioning systems, aerosol units and fluorocarbon-blown foam products," Kaiser Aluminum and Chemical Corporation stated in a pamphlet it issued on the ozone issue. The most commonly used refrigerants today are F-11 and F-12, and although possible alternatives include F-22, ammonia, sulfur dioxide, methyl chloride and hydrocarbons, all are less stable or have other drawbacks. In addition, current refrigerators and air conditioners are engineered specifically for F-11 and F-12, and a ban on them would entail extensive changes in present systems.

As for aerosols, alternatives include compressed gases such as nitrogen, carbon dioxide or nitrous oxide; soluble liquefied gases such as vinyl chloride, propane and butane; and mechnical devices such as finger pumps, squeeze bottles and roll-ons. However, these have various drawbacks including corrosiveness (carbon dioxide), large drops (nitrogen), toxicity (vinyl chloride), insufficient solubility (nitrous oxide) and flammability (propane and butane). Mechanical devices, industry spokesmen argue, have been proved less desirable than aerosols in free market competition.

So the fluorocarbon-ozone controversy, like many other issues in recent years involving technology and the environment, tends to become more complicated the more it is studied. The scientific experts disagree, the industry spokesmen press for more time, the policy makers are confused and the public is exasperated. It seems likely that some restrictions on fluorocarbons will be put into effect within the next few years, but the nature and timing of such action cannot be foreseen today. Meanwhile, if the ozone-depletion theories prove correct, there inevitably will be some thinning of the earth's protective ozone layer—however serious or insignificant the result. In answering the ozone question, it appears that humankind was lucky—because of a chance scientific discovery we have been forewarned.

Selected Bibliography

Articles

Alexander, Tom, "What We Know—And Do Not Know—About the Ozone Shield," *Fortune*, August 1975.

Brodeur, Paul, "Annals of Chemistry—Inert," *The New Yorker*, April 7, 1975.

Drosnin, Michael, "Not With a Bang, But With a Pssssst!" *New Times*, March 7, 1975.

Edson, Lee, "Not With a Bang But a Pfffft?" *The New York Times Magazine*, Dec. 21, 1975.

Gosnell, Marianna, "Ozone—The Trick Is Containing It Where We Need It," *Smithsonian*, June 1975.

Mitchell, Sean, "The Politics of Freon," *The Nation*, June 28, 1975.

Molina, Mario J. and F. Sherwood Rowland, "Stratospheric Sink for Chlorofluoromethanes: Chlorine Atom-Catalysed Destruction of Ozone," *Nature*, June 28, 1974.

"Ozone Alert," *Time*, Feb. 23, 1976.

Sherwood, Martin, et al., "The Ozone-Layer Controversy," *Atlas World Press Review*, December 1975.

Thomas, Dana L., "The Sky Is Falling!" *Barron's*, March 3, 1975.

Weinberg, Janet H., "Ozone Verdict: On Faith or Fact?" *Science News*, May 17, 1975.

Studies and Reports

Federal Interagency Task Force on Inadvertent Modification of the Stratosphere, "Fluorocarbons and the Environment," June 1975.

Kaiser Aluminum and Chemical Corporation, "At Issue: Fluorocarbons," June 1975.

Shamel, R. E., J. K. O'Neill and R. Williams, "Preliminary Economic Impact Assessment of Possible Regulatory Action to Control Atmospheric Emissions of Selected Halocarbons," Arthur D. Little, Inc., September 1975.

U.S. House of Representatives, Subcommittee on Public Health and Environment of the Committee on Interstate and Foreign Commerce, Hearings on "Fluorocarbons—Impact on Health and Environment," Dec. 11-12, 1974.

COASTAL ZONE MANAGEMENT

by

Mary Costello

Mar. 19
1 9 7 6

COASTAL ZONE MANAGEMENT

THE LATE 1970s are likely to witness a growing involvement by the nation's cities and states in planning, developing and implementing the federally funded programs that affect them. No doubt Washington will continue to supply the largest share of the money for these projects, but the federal government probably will have less control over how they are carried out. Proposals for returning more "power to the people" and their local representatives elicited wide bipartisan support during this year's presidential campaign. This support and the programs that reflect it represent a shift away from the "big brother knows best" attitude that has characterized the federal government's relationship with the states and cities since the New Deal.

Coastal zone management is an existing example of this trend. In response to the problems of pollution, overdevelopment, shore erosion and population expansion along America's seashores, Congress approved the Coastal Zone Management Act of 1972. It gave 30 coastal states[1] the responsibility for developing plans to protect and promote the 20,000 miles of United States coastline. The act defined coastal zones as coastal waters and adjacent shorelands, including tidal areas, salt marshes, wetlands and beaches. The Great Lakes and their sounds, bays, lagoons and estuaries were included in the definition.

The 1972 law provides for development grants (section 305) and administrative grants (section 306) to cover two-thirds of the cost of the programs. To receive these funds, the states are to give "full consideration to ecological, cultural, historic and esthetic values, as well as to needs for economic development." The act created an Office of Coastal Zone Management within the Department of Commerce's National Oceanic and Atmospheric Administration to administer the law.

Under section 305, Congress authorized development grants of $9-million a year for three years. This amount was increased

---

[1] Alabama, Alaska, California, Connecticut, Delaware, Florida, Georgia, Hawaii, Illinois, Indiana, Louisiana, Maine, Maryland, Massachusetts, Michigan, Minnesota, Mississippi, New Hampshire, New Jersey, New York, North Carolina, Ohio, Oregon, Pennsylvania, Rhode Island, South Carolina, Texas, Virginia, Washington and Wisconsin. The act also applies to the territories of American Samoa, Guam, the Virgin Islands and the Commonwealth of Puerto Rico.

to $12-million annually in 1975, and the states were later given an extra year to complete their programs. Each state applying for an annual development grant is required to define the boundaries of its coastal zone and explain what it plans to do about land and water uses in the area. Once the development program has been adopted by the state and approved by the Secretary of Commerce, the state becomes eligible for administrative grants under section 306.

The program is an attempt to reconcile the need for economic development with the need for shoreline preservation. The Coastal Energy Impact Act, signed by President Ford on July 26, 1976, provides additional federal incentive for reconciling these seemingly contradictory needs. The 1976 law authorizes the federal government to provide up to $1.2-billion in grants and loans over the next 10 years to assist states in dealing with the effects of offshore oil and gas development.

In describing the legislation, Ford noted that it "limits the extent to which the federal government will become involved in decisions that should be made at the state and local levels." He said, "The individual states and localities will determine whether their principal need is for schools, roads, hospitals, new parks and other similar facilities" in coastal areas. The coastal zone management program puts strong emphasis on public participation in state and local decision-making. A "consistency clause" in the 1972 law specifies that all federal programs affecting a state's coastal zone—except those directly involving national security—must be consistent with the state program. The "federal consistency clause," the Office of Coastal Zone Management said in its latest annual report, "is a strong incentive for states to participate voluntarily in the coastal zone management program."[2]

Diversity of State Plans to Protect the Coasts

Twenty-eight coastal states are working on or revising their development plans.[3] Each coastal zone has its particular problems and concerns but a common thread runs through all the program efforts. This is the question of how to deal with the demands of developers, oil companies, builders, trade unions and realtors who argue that growth restrictions must be kept at a minimum to prevent economic stagnation and of environmentalists who contend that restrictions must be stringent to save the fragile coastal ecosystem.

The only state plan to receive final federal approval to date

---

[2] Office of Coastal Zone Management, "Report to the Congress on Coastal Zone Management, July 1974-June 1975," April 1976, p. 2.

[3] Washington state's development plan was approved June 1. Indiana was suspended from the program this fall and American Samoa is not participating because of lack of funds.

Coastal Zone Management Funding

State	Agency	Fiscal 1975	Fiscal 1976
		(thousands of dollars)	
Ala.	Alabama Development Office	180	----
Alaska	Policy Development and Planning Division	----	1,800
Calif.	California Coastal Zone Conservation Commission	1,350	1,800
Conn.	Department of Environmental Protection	----	588
Del.	State Planning Office	----	585
Fla.	Bureau of Coastal Zone Planning	----	1,144
Ga.	Office of Planning & Budget	541	100
Hawaii	Department of Planning and Economic Development	600	750
Ill.	Illinois Coastal Zone Management Program	576	----
Ind.	State Planning Services Agency	330	----
La.	State Planning Office	513	1,065
Maine	State Planning Office	493	906
Md.	Department of Natural Resources	609	231
Mass.	Executive Office of Environmental Affairs	587	862
Mich.	Department of Natural Resources	600	654
Minn.	State Planning Agency	225	341
Miss.	Marine Resources Council	196	120
N.H.	Office of Comprehensive Planning	180	222
N.J.	Department of Environmental Protection	706	506
N.Y.	Department of State Planning	825	1,730
N.C.	Department of Natural and Economic Resources	755	1,041
Ohio	Department of Natural Resources	----	639
Ore.	Land Conservation and Development Commission	453	1,346
Penn.	Division of Outdoor Recreation	337	438
R.I.	Department of Administration	456	178
S.C.	Wildlife and Marine Resources Department	336	715
Texas	Coastal Management Program	1,068	1,788
Va.	Office of Commerce and Resources	376	605
Wash.	Department of Ecology	----	1,162
Wis.	State Planning Office	513	332
Guam	Bureau of Planning	215	----
Puerto Rico	Department of Natural Resources	525	636
Virgin Islands	Virgin Islands Planning Office	135	180

SOURCE: Office of Coastal Zone Management

has been Washington's. The 15 coastal counties comprise only 29 per cent of the land but are inhabited by two-thirds of the state's residents. When the legislature approved the state Shoreline Management Act of 1971—a law that preceded the federal Coastal Zone Management Act—the coastline was faced with water pollution problems on Puget Sound, unplanned development and overcrowding, the danger of oil spills, a planned Trident nuclear submarine base on the Kitsap Peninsula and proposed nuclear power plants near the shore. Under

The States and Coastal Zone Management

Much of the inspiration for enactment of the Coastal Zone Management Act of 1972 came from a report by the Commission on Marine Science, Engineering and Resources which was submitted to President Nixon in January 1969. The report, entitled "Our Nation and the Sea," said "the key to more effective use of our coastline is the introduction of a management system permitting conscious and informed choices among development alternatives."

The commission proposed enactment of a Coastal Management Act "to provide policy objectives for the coastal zone and authorize federal grants-in-aid to facilitate the establishment of state coastal zone authorities empowered to manage the coastal waters and adjacent land." The states, the commission said, are "the central link joining the many participants" and "must be the focus for responsibility and action in the coastal zone."

the 1971 act, the Washington State Department of Ecology was directed to coordinate the coastal management program. The final state plan gave both ecologists and developers some but not all of what they wanted. Oil companies were unhappy with limitations on tanker traffic in Puget Sound and are appealing these restrictions. Environmentalists wanted the shoreline to extend farther inland than the plan specified, 200 feet from the mean high tide line.

"The state coastal zone management programs in Delaware, North Carolina, Oregon and Rhode Island have attracted the most attention," the federal Council on Environmental Quality observed. "Some of these programs depend upon a system of state permits to regulate land use changes, although the North Carolina program relies on 30 coastal counties to conduct the program under state auspices.... The Delaware program is perhaps the most well known because it prohibits heavy industry in a coastal strip two miles wide. Much of this protected coastal zone lies along the heavily traveled Delaware Bay downstream from existing industrial areas."[4]

The council's assessment was written before the California plan was approved by the state legislature and signed by Gov. Edmund G. Brown Jr. on Sept. 29, 1976. The California program has become not only the most publicized but the most extensive that has been enacted by any state. The plan, which most observers expect to be approved by the Secretary of Commerce within a short time, grew out of voter approval of the Coastal Initiative (Proposition 20) in 1972. Proposition 20 called for the creation of (1) a California Coastal Plan and (2) a Coastal

---

[4] Council on Environmental Quality, "Environmental Quality—1976," September 1976, pp. 74-75. The Council was set up by the National Environmental Policy Act of 1969 to advise the President and Congress on environmental matters. This is its seventh annual report.

Zone Conservation Commission and six regional commissions to regulate development for three years and to submit a long-term plan to the state legislature by December 1975.

A bill introduced at Sacramento early this year to protect California's 1,072 miles of coastline incorporated most of the recommendations from the Coastal Zone Conservation Commission. The bill was widely viewed as favoring conservation over development. Supporters included environmental groups, recreational users of the coast (except boaters), planners and the League of Women Voters. The principal opponents were land developers, oil companies, utilities, the building trade unions, realtors, property-rights groups and "*laissez-faire* economists."[5] Opponents formed the California Council for Environmental and Economic Balance which sought to restrict state control to recreational areas and public access to the beaches.

To placate oil interests, utilities, city governments and trade and labor groups, the original bill was amended more than 300 times before it was finally approved in September. Among the most significant amendments were those reducing the area where building could be restricted (from as far as five miles inland to generally no more than 1,000 yards) and the exemption of urban areas from certain provisions. The Coastal Commission was also deprived of veto power over power-plant and most oil-facility sites.

Competing Concerns: Environment and Economy

The 23 Atlantic, Pacific and Gulf Coast states as well as the seven Great Lakes states have specific regulations for obtaining permits for building projects near the shore—many that predate the 1972 federal law. The program approved by the California legislature in September specifies that regional commissions must be convinced that development will have no "substantial adverse environmental effect" and is consistent with the state plan before they can issue a building permit. Local communities can appeal permit decisions to the permanent state commission for review. For the first time "the state is permanently and directly involved in land-use regulation," commission consultant Robert Shelton contends. "It's undoubtedly the first step to eventual statewide land-use controls."[6] Other states are expected to follow California's example. Most of them have already enacted regulations that clearly put the burden of proof on permit applicants to show that no ecological damage will be done. Delaware's Coastal Zone Act is among the most stringent in this regard.

[5] So described by Paul A. Sabatier, "Regulating Development Along the California Coast," *Journal of Soil and Water Conservation,* July-August 1976, p. 151.

[6] Quoted in "An Environmental Law Business Can Live With," *Business Week,* Sept. 13, 1976, pp. 39-40.

That act prohibits all construction of heavy industry in the coastal zone. Other proposed industrial development is regulated by the Delaware State Planning Office. Permit applications must be approved by local authorities and include a description of the project and an environmental impact statement. The statement is to include an assessment of the impact of the proposed use of the land on such natural resources as water quality, fisheries, wildlife and scenery. The State Planning Office is authorized to hold public hearings on permit applications. Decisions to approve or reject these applications are to be taken only after consideration is given to the environmental, economic and esthetic effects, the surrounding facilities that would be required and the effect they would be likely to have on surrounding land uses and the coastal plan.

Much of the North Carolina coast is sparsely populated and beset by high unemployment and a need for economic growth. But most other coastal areas, including the Delaware shore, are faced with heavy development pressures. The situation along the California coast is typical. Scientists at the Scripps Institution of Oceanography at La Jolla reported recently that massive building along the Southern California coast has caused a steady erosion of the shoreline and is weakening the cliffs which protect the land from tidal onslaughts. The erosion, they said, was proceeding at a rate of two to three feet a year.

Environmentalists have been arguing that similar erosion will affect the Atlantic Coast and the Gulf of Mexico if some of the developments now being planned are completed. Conservationists in Delaware, Maryland and Virginia have strongly opposed a project by the Army Corps of Engineers to cut through the mid-Atlantic wetlands to create a 150-mile waterway for private and commercial boats. The conservationists contend that the waterway would destroy the wetlands and barrier islands that protect the shoreline from ocean storms.

In a study of barrier islands—long chains of relatively flat, sandy islands that flank the coast from Maine to Texas—the Conservation Foundation found that of the 281 islands it studied, "[S]eventy islands or significant portions of them have been partially developed, heavily developed or just plain urbanized. Many of these are virtually destroyed as resources with little hope for restoration." Islands where the "threat of development has arrived or is imminent" include St. Phillips Island, N.C.; Kiawah Island, S.C.; and Marco Island, St. Georges Island and Matagorda Island, Fla.[7] Some 25 conservation groups, including the foundation, have formed a national organization called Barrier Island Watch to stop potentially destructive develop-

---

[7] John R. Clark and Robb Turner, "Barrier Islands: A Threatened Resource," *Conservation Foundation Letter*, August 1976.

ment of the barrier islands and to make sure that these islands are given special attention in state coastal zone management plans.

Debates about development versus conservation have been mostly matters of state and local concern. An exception has been the issue of offshore drilling, involving the federal government. The rise in oil prices during recent years and the fear of natural gas shortages have put pressure on the government to encourage more offshore exploration through lease sales in an effort to meet the nation's energy needs. In the past few years, environmentalist concern about the effects of offshore production has undergone some change.

In its report to Congress, the Office of Coastal Zone Management noted that the major concern about offshore drilling had shifted from the possibility of oil spills to the problem of coping with onshore development and disruption. Communities faced with offshore drilling can expect substantial population increases. This growth will affect land use patterns, employment, housing, taxes and government services like schools, police and fire protection, sewer capacity and roads.[8]

In approving the Coastal Energy Impact Act of 1976, Congress attempted to spur offshore energy activity and at the same time protect coastal states from environmental and economic disruption. Loans and grants to affected states will depend upon the volume of oil and gas produced off their shores and the level of new energy-producing activity in the states. The law requires that all federal leases for exploration, development and production affecting a state's coastal zone be consistent with the state's coastal zone management program before any license or permit can be issued.

Effort to Reduce Water and Shoreline Pollution

Offshore oil and gas drilling opens up thousands of jobs in coastal areas. The onshore industrial and residential development that this population growth encourages seems inevitably to produce not only land-use but pollution problems. Faced with coastal and inland water pollution, Congress approved the Federal Water Pollution Control Act in 1972. That law provided $24.7-billion over three years as the first stage in an effort to clean up the country's waters by 1985. It directed the Environmental Protection Agency (EPA) to subsidize sewage-treatment plant construction and file suits against industrial polluters.[9] But water pollution has been more difficult and

---

[8] See League of Women Voters Education Fund report, "The Onshore Impact of Offshore Oil," 1976, p. 4.

[9] For background, see "Pollution Control: Costs and Benefits," *E.R.R.*, 1976 Vol. I, pp. 155-158.

Kepone Pollution

In July 1975, illness struck seven workers employed at Life Science Products, in Hopewell, Va., a company that manufactured kepone, a highly toxic insecticide, for Allied Chemical Co. It was found that the workers' trembling and shaking were a result of their exposure to the chemical.

The problem of kepone poisoning extended far beyond Hopewell. Both Life Science and Allied, which developed kepone and produced it from 1966 until Life Science took over in 1973, had discharged kepone into the James River which empties into the Chesapeake Bay.

As a result of the kepone discharge, the Life Science plant was closed, kepone production was halted in Virginia, Gov. Mills E. Godwin ordered a ban on fishing in the James River, the federal government prohibited the manufacture of all pesticides containing kepone, and Congress and the state legislature began lengthy hearings on tightening environmental regulations. Life Science, Allied and the city of Hopewell were brought to court and charged with hundreds of violations of federal and state water pollution laws. They have been convicted on some of the charges. Some were dismissed or dropped and some cases are continuing.

Kepone poisoning has not been limited to the air, water and soil around Hopewell nor even to the James River. Traces have been found in the lower Chesapeake Bay and the Atlantic Ocean. Kepone causes neurological disorders and there is fear it may be harmful to the liver, spleen, brain and male fertility. It is also suspected of causing cancer.

costlier to control than was envisioned as recently as 1972. *The Wall Street Journal* reported that more than $1-billion has been spent to treat municipal sewage going into Lake Erie but, it is now estimated, $17-billion more is needed. The original cost estimate was $1.1-billion. Moreover, the expected cost to industries along the lake is $2-billion in order for them to meet federal standards for water pollution control.[10]

Lake Erie may offer one of the worst cases of pollution in large bodies of water but it is by no means unique. Last summer numerous beaches along the Atlantic Coast, including the popular Jones Beach near New York City, were closed temporarily when sewage washed ashore. Environmentalists have accused the Army Corps of Engineers and EPA, which have joint jurisdiction over ocean dumping, of violating the 1972 Ocean Dumping Act. That law established regulations on disposal to protect human health and welfare, the marine environment and the economic potential of ocean resources. The town of Hopewell, Va., was clearly in violation of this act and pleaded

---

[10] Reported by Craig P. Charney, *The Wall Street Journal*, Aug. 31, 1976.

no contest on June 25, 1976, to federal charges that it had permitted the highly toxic chemical kepone to be discharged into the James River which empties into the Chesapeake Bay.[11]

The Federal Water Pollution Control Act sets as a national goal the elimination of all pollutant discharges into U.S. waters by 1985 and an interim goal of making the waters safe for fish, shellfish, wildlife and people by July 1, 1983. The Council on Environmental Quality reported that ocean dumping, except for dredged material, decreased 23 per cent in 1975—almost down to the 1968 level. However, dredged materials account for about 90 per cent of the materials dumped in coastal waters. And of the 23 per cent reduction, it is not clear how much resulted from reduced economic activity, especially in construction, nor is it clear whether land disposal of solid wastes has increased as it must when ocean dumping decreases.

Another issue of great concern to environmentalists is the danger of oil spills along the coastlines. The number of spills reported in U.S. waters in 1975 was 25 per cent below the 1974 figure—down from 13,966 to 10,538. But the amount of oil discharged into the waters increased by 33 per cent—from almost 17 billion gallons to more than 24 billion. This year also has had its share of oil spills. One of the major spills occurred June 23 when an oil barge ran aground on the New York side of the St. Lawrence River and discharged 250,000 gallons of oil. A spill of comparable size was caused by the puncture of a tanker off Perth Amboy, N.J., on Oct. 29.

Jurisdiction Over the Shorelines

S INCE ANCIENT TIMES the seas have been the garbage bins and dumping grounds of mankind. Tradition held that they belonged to no one and therefore man could use them as he saw fit. In the early 1800s, the United States followed the lead of most of the European maritime powers in declaring that the country had sovereignty over territorial waters three miles from the coast.[12] But efforts to protect the shore from pollution rather than from foreign interference lagged for many decades. The duties assigned to the Army Corps of Engineers are illustrative. The corps was established during the Revolutionary War to

---

[11] Hopewell was also in violation of an international convention drawn up by most of the world's maritime nations and signed by the United States on Dec. 29, 1972. It prohibits the dumping of poisonous materials into the oceans and requires a permit for the discharge of less harmful materials.

[12] The three-mile limit was commonly known as the "cannon shot" rule on the assumption that three miles was as far as a cannonball could be fired.

provide combat support for the Army. Congress in 1824 gave it the task of improving navigation in the Ohio and Mississippi Rivers. Responsibility for flood control and hydraulic mining regulation came later, and in 1930 "coastal protection" was added.

Enactment of federal and state laws aimed at saving the shores from large-scale dumping, dredging and overdevelopment was slow and uneven. It was not until 1886 that the industrial pollution in New York harbor prompted Congress to impose fines on anyone dumping "refuse or mill-waste of any kind" in the harbor. In 1913, Oregon became the first state to limit coastal development by declaring all beaches and public highways ineligible for private purchase.

A federal program setting aside coastal areas as wilderness preserves and blocking most forms of commercial or harmful recreational activity in those designated areas began in 1937. On Aug. 27 of that year, 28,500 acres at Cape Hatteras, N.C., were declared a national seashore. The program lagged, however, until the early 1960s. In 1961, 44,600 acres on Cape Cod, Mass., became a coastal preserve. Since that time, the following areas have been included in the national seashores and lakeshores system:

Point Reyes, Calif. (1962)	Apostle Islands, Wis. (1970)
Padre Island, Texas (1962)	Sleeping Bear Dunes, Mich.
Assateague Island, Md.-Va.	(1970)
(1965)	Gulf Islands, Fla.-Miss.
Fire Island, N.Y. (1965)	(1971)
Cape Lookout, N.C. (1966)	Cumberland Island, Ga. (1972)
Pictured Rocks, Mich. (1966)	Canaveral National Seashore,
Indiana Dunes, Ind. (1966)	Fla. (1975)

Federal aid to the states to lessen water pollution in coastal areas was first authorized by the Water Pollution Control Act of 1948. That legislation provided $22.5-million over five years. It was to be used primarily for low-interest loans to states and localities for construction of sewage and waste-treatment facilities and for grants to the states for pollution studies. In the mid-1960s the federal money available to coastal areas for water pollution abatement increased substantially.

The amount needed to deal with water pollution would have been considerably less if the country had preserved more coastal and island wetlands—shallows, mudflats, estuaries, swamps and marshes. In addition to being an important source of food and water storage, the wetlands nurture bacteria that break down air-pollutant sulfates and water-pollutant nitrates. But American wetlands have been systematically dredged and filled to make way for commercial and residential development. According to a study prepared by J. W. Morris, chief of engineers for the Army Corps of Engineers: "When the United States was first settled, there were about 127 million acres of wetlands, but by 1955 only 75 million acres remained."[13]

In 1959, a Department of Commerce report prepared for the corps took note of the wetland destruction in the San Francisco Bay area. The report, entitled "Future Development of the San Francisco Bay Area," found that between 1850 and 1957, over 242.8 square miles of marsh and submerged lands had been filled and that the bay had been reduced from 680 to 437 square miles. The report predicted that an additional 70 square miles—primarily marshland—would be filled by the end of the century. "By about 1990, little unreclaimed marshland will remain in the Bay area."

Response to 1960s' Environmental Movement

The San Francisco study led concerned citizens to establish a Save San Francisco Bay Association, a lobby group set up to mobilize public sentiment and pressure public officials to slow dredging and filling operations. Five years after the association was formed in 1960, it succeeded in persuading the state legislature to approve "the first coastal management effort in the United States," the San Francisco Bay Conservation and Development Commission. Largely because of the group's campaign, the rate of fill declined.

During the 1960s, the environment became a national issue and a multitude of federal, state and local programs were started in an attempt to prevent further deterioration of coastal areas. Typically, a maze of jurisdictional disputes, conflicting policies and duplicate mandates resulted.[14] The billions of dollars spent and the hundreds of laws enacted did not keep pace with the problems faced by coastal communities. Industrial and residential development proceeded even faster during the decade. And with development came pollution and shoreline erosion. Conservationists continually criticized federal programs for pollution control and coastal conservation as underfinanced and poorly planned.

They also criticized the number of leases the federal government was selling to private companies for extraction of oil and gas from coastal waters. Between 1954[15] and 1968 over six

---

[13] "The Corps in Perspective since 1775," a paper presented to the American Society of Civil Engineers' annual convention in Philadelphia on Sept. 28, 1976.

[14] See William J. Brennan's account of the situation in Oregon, "Balancing Man's Demands for the Sea and Shore," *NOAA Magazine* (of the National Oceanic and Atmospheric Administration), October 1974, p. 3.

[15] In 1954 the Supreme Court upheld the Submerged Lands Act of 1953, effectively settling the "tidelands" dispute between coastal states and the federal government over control of underwater tracts. See "Offshore Oil Search," *E.R.R.*, 1973 Vol. II, pp. 545-550.

million acres were leased in Pacific and Gulf Coast waters. Warnings about oil spills, leaks, eruptions and onshore disruptions went largely unheeded until an oil well being drilled in the Santa Barbara Channel erupted on Jan. 28, 1969. The well spewed thousands of barrels of oil into the Pacific, blackening nearby California beaches and killing birds and fish.

Oil Spill as Catalyst for Coastal Legislation

The Santa Barbara spill produced a strong and immediate demand for a cessation of offshore drilling in coastal waters. A few months after the eruption, the California State Lands Commission ruled against further drilling in state tidelands. The Department of the Interior temporarily suspended drilling and pumping operations in the channel and issued regulations tightening safety rules on drilling.

The Santa Barbara accident was an important factor in passage of the National Environmental Policy Act in December 1969 and the Water Quality Improvement Act in March 1970. The former directed federal agencies to consider the impact on the environment of all major activities and to include in every recommendation a written analysis of the likely effects.[16] The 1970 law authorized the federal government to clean up oil spills that jeopardize coastal waters and beaches, and made the polluter liable for up to $14-million of the cleanup costs. The law also placed new controls on sewage coming from vessels and strengthened the government's authority to regulate offshore drilling.

Florida and several other coastal states have enacted stricter regulations. Under a Florida law, polluters are required to reimburse the state for clean-up costs and private property damage; unlike the federal law, the Florida statute imposed liability even if the oil spill resulted from an act of God, war, U.S. negligence or an act or omission by a third party. The Supreme Court upheld the Florida law on April 18, 1973. In that case, Florida was supported by briefs filed by 18 other states.

These laws and regulations led to a considerable slowdown in offshore oil and gas drilling and stiffened the resistance of Atlantic Coast states to exploration off their shores.[17] But opposition to the slowdowns and stoppages grew. In testimony before the House Interior and Insular Affairs Committee on April 18, 1972, as Secretary of the Treasury, John B. Connally complained that there had been enough delay in offshore production because of environmental fears. "Let us start leasing, exploring, drilling, pipelining, shipping, refining and using more prudently the

---

[16] For background, see "Environmental Policy," *E.R.R.*, 1974 Vol. II, pp. 945-964.
[17] The first lease for exploration in the Atlantic was not granted until August 1976.

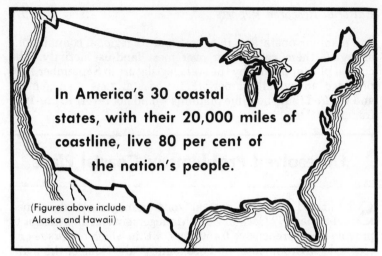

In America's 30 coastal states, with their 20,000 miles of coastline, live 80 per cent of the nation's people.

(Figures above include Alaska and Hawaii)

resultant clean energy this country needs to keep our people employed, our economy going and our society alive and thriving," Connally asserted. The Arab oil embargo in late 1973 moved the government to push for more offshore drilling.

Offshore drilling was only one of the problems facing coastal areas. In the early 1970s, programs to deal with the many difficulties facing coastal communities seemed underfinanced, inadequate, overlapping and tied up in bureaucratic red tape. Beach erosion projects were one example. Harold E. Marshall of the National Bureau of Standards noted that, as of 1971, the Army Corps of Engineers had cooperated with and shared the costs with non-federal interests for the construction of 61 projects protecting 110 miles of shore. The federal government had contributed $28-million of the total cost of $45-million. Seventeen other projects protecting 171 miles had been authorized and were under way, and 43 more protecting some 300 miles had not been started. But in 1971, "significant erosion was occurring along 20,500 miles" of shoreline and the cost of protecting this coastline would run into billions.[18]

Coastal preservation efforts were hindered as much by lack of coordination as by inadequate funding. The plethora of competing interests and diverse programs that characterized California's shoreline management plans before 1972 was typical of the situation in most states. Before voters approved Proposition 20 in 1972, "coastal resources in California were being managed primarily by: (1) private and public landowners; (2) cities and counties; and (3) a welter of special-function state and federal agencies."[19] Proposition 20 centralized development

[18] Harold E. Marshall, "Efficiency Impact of Cost-Sharing on Shoreline Management," *Coastal Zone Management Journal*, 1976 Vol. 2, No. 4, pp. 369-370.

[19] Robert C. Ellickson, "Ticket to Thermidor: A Commentary on the Proposed California Coastal Plan," *Southern California Law Review*, May 1976, p. 735.

and planning operations in a state and six regional commissions and gave them veto power over most land-use activity. The coastal plan approved by the state legislature in September 1976 provided an overall framework for coastal zone management and insured that shoreline planning would not revert to pre-1972 fragmentation.

Unresolved Problems in Coastal Plans

STATE PLANS for coastal zone management developed under the 1972 Coastal Zone Management Act all attempt to provide a comprehensive framework within which to pursue and reconcile environmental and economic goals. None of the plans to date has gone as far as California's. Many are still beset by jurisdictional problems and fragmentation. In Delaware, for example, three major laws have been enacted since 1971 to protect the coastal zone. These are the Coastal Zone Act, which prohibits and controls industrial development; the Beach Preservation Act, which allows the state to prevent alterations that could damage the protective primary dune line; and the Coastal Wetlands Act, which gives the state control of land use in the coastal salt marsh.

While these three laws "present a formidable barrier to undesired development," John L. Pedrick Jr. has written, procedural fragmentation "may rob them of some portion of their effectiveness." Pedrick recommends that they be combined "into one consolidated law...[that] would place all coastal zone land-use permit decisions in the hands of one administering agency and one statewide appeals board."[20]

Federal programs in coastal areas are also beset by jurisdictional overlap and fragmentation. This problem is particularly apparent in regulations on offshore oil exploration. The Departments of Interior and Commerce share jurisdiction over deep-sea mining, but according to a recent report by Richard A. Frank, director of the International Project of the Center for Law and Social Policy, "neither...has been vested with clear overall responsibility" and "neither is well suited for the task of environmental regulation." Interior's Ocean Mining Administration and Commerce's National Oceanic and Atmospheric Administration both have evidenced "a bias" in favor of development and against environmental protection, Frank contends.

---

[20] John L. Pedrick Jr., "Land Use Control in the Coastal Zone: The Delaware Example," *Coastal Zone Management Journal*, 1976 Vol. 2, No. 4, pp. 346-347, 361. Pedrick is a research associate at the National Resources Law Institute, Portland, Ore.

He argues that "environmental protection can best be assured if the same agency is not assigned the responsibility both of promotion and also of environmental regulation." Such jurisdiction "presents an inevitable, potential conflict of interest and results in unobjective decision making, benefitting those who favor development." Frank proposes that the Environmental Protection Agency be given the power to determine whether applicants for offshore leases comply with environmental standards while another agency "would pass on economic and royalty considerations."[21]

In testimony before the House Subcommittee on Oceanography, Sept. 9, 1976, Secretary of Commerce Elliot L. Richardson stressed the need for a comprehensive and integrated policy on control and use of ocean resources. Richardson proposed that a Cabinet-level agency be set up to develop an overall oceans policy. This might resolve some of the differences between Congress and the executive branch over whether the United States should act alone and proceed with deep-sea mining if an international Law of the Sea treaty is not concluded soon.[22] But a Cabinet-level agency with responsibility for developing an overall oceans policy could have difficulty complying with the consistency clause (see p. 68) in the 1972 Coastal Zone Management Act. Even in the absence of such an agency, the clause is likely to be challenged in the courts, particularly in regard to offshore and deep-sea mining, if the states enact strict restrictions on development in their coastal zone management programs.

Issue of Private Property and Public Interest

Another likely subject of litigation involves private property versus public interest in state land-use regulations. The Fifth and Fourteenth Amendments to the Constitution prohibit the taking of private property for public use without just compensation and due process of law. While the courts have declined to define private ownership of property as an absolute right, the question remains: "How far may society go in reclaiming economic value created by its members without transgressing fundamental rights protected by the Bill of Rights?"[23]

The problem of just compensation involves not only the potentially lucrative uses that privately owned land could have been put to but the amount of money that the state or federal government will have to spend to prevent private owners from

---

[21] Richard A. Frank, "Deepsea Mining and the Environment: A Report of the Working Group on Environmental Regulation and Deepsea Mining," April 1976, pp. 25, 37-38.

[22] See "Oceanic Law," *E.R.R.*, 1974 Vol. I, p. 405.

[23] Gerald Bowdon, "Legal Battles on the California Coast: A Review of the Rules," *Coastal Zone Management Journal*, 1976 Vol. 2, No. 3, p. 275. Bowdon teaches environmental studies at the University of California at Santa Cruz.

Public Access to Beaches

An amendment to the Coastal Zone Management Act, approved in July 1976, requires states participating in the program to establish a planning process for dealing with questions of public access to beaches. The most common forms of preventing access are zoning restrictions and requirements that outside visitors pay a fee for using the beach.

Restrictions on public access to beaches vary from state to state but tend to be strongest in residential areas along the East Coast. By law, the states of Oregon and Texas require that all beaches be open to the public. By the early 1970s, the courts began ruling against state restrictions on beach use. In 1971, owners of expensive beach houses at Malibu, near Los Angeles, lost the right to block public access to the shore. Early the next year, a 1970 law restricting the Long Beach, N.Y., shore to residents and their guests was struck down. And in 1972, the New Jersey Supreme Court ruled that even modest fees imposed on a non-resident violated the public trust principle.

Opponents of public access to beaches are likely to be increasingly on the defensive as states develop and debate their coastal zone management programs. Action taken in California may be indicative of this trend. The coastal plan approved in September 1976 favors greater public access to beaches. And California voters approved a proposition on the Nov. 2 ballot which permits state acquisition of land for public use.

developing their land. The French government has set up a Coastal Preservation Association, similar to Britain's National Trust, to buy tracts of land along the coastline and put them under state protection. However, the association has a first-year budget of only $2.4-million.

A privately funded American organization, the Nature Conservancy, attempts "to preserve and protect ecologically and environmentally significant land and the diversity of life it supports" not only on the coasts but throughout the country. Set up in 1951, the organization accepts as gifts or buys up at no more than fair market value land it considers worth preserving. All development, except trails and visitor centers, is prohibited. The organization has purchased 13 of the 18 barrier islands off the coast of Virginia as well as islands off South Carolina, Georgia, Maine and elsewhere.

A proposal that would involve the government in land purchases but, unlike the British and French programs, would give most of the control to the affected areas was before Congress in 1976 and, failing to win approval, is expected to be reintroduced in 1977. It was the Nantucket Sound Islands Trust bill, sponsored by Sen. Edward M. Kennedy (D Miss.) and Rep. Gerry E. Studds (D Mass.) to set up local "trust commissions" on Nantucket, Martha's Vineyard and the Elizabeth Islands off Cape Cod. The commissions would have the first chance to buy land that came on the market. Federal money would be used to acquire the land and keep it out of the hands of developers, but the local commissions would decide what land to buy and what to do with it.

Costs and Benefits of Shoreline Management

There is no way of estimating the overall cost of coastal zone management, but even its strongest proponents concede that it will be expensive. They insist, however, that doing nothing will be far more costly. Demographers have projected that by the year 2000, half of the American people will live on 5 per cent of the land in three urban coastal belts: the Atlantic, the Pacific and the Great Lakes. Without plans to reconcile the increasing demands for jobs and services with the need to preserve the fragile shoreline ecosystem, it is argued, some coastal areas will be damaged beyond repair while others will require extensive and expensive salvage operations.

The nation's wetlands provide one example of the costs and benefits of preservation. These coastal fringe areas are vital for the fishing industry, for water quality and for shoreline protection. The dredging and filling of tidal wetlands not only have destroyed fish and shellfish resources and contributed to water pollution and shore erosion problems, but these lands are difficult and expensive to replace. In an article in the November 1975 issue of Louisiana's *Shreveport Magazine,* Roul Tunley noted that "the cost of planting, to turn the land into a working marsh, ranges from $500 to $2,000 an acre."[24]

Coastal zone management represents an effort to help the states and cities save coastal areas before the damage grows beyond their ability to repair it. There can be little doubt that it will be less expensive for the affected areas to take action now rather than later.

Jimmy Carter's statements during the campaign about the need for stricter environmental protection measures and the desirability of giving more decision-making power to the states and localities indicate that his administration will be sympathetic to their efforts. Despite the problems that continue to plague state programs and despite the conflicts over economic and ecological needs, those involved in coastal zone management have reason for optimism.

---

[24] Roul Tunley, "Victory in the Wetlands," *Shreveport Magazine,* November 1975, p. 57. See Shirley K. Werthamer, "The State Role in Land Use: New York in the Seventies," *National Civic Review,* October 1976, p. 449.

Selected Bibliography

Books

Brahtz, John F., *Coastal Zone Management: Multiple Use With Conservation*, Wiley, 1972.
Carson, Rachel, *The Sea Around Us*, Oxford University Press, 1961.
Herbich, John B., *Coastal and Deep Ocean Dredging*, Gulf Publishers, 1975.
Mitchell, Edward J. (ed.), *The Question of Offshore Oil*, American Enterprise Institute for Public Policy Research, 1976.
Padelford, Norman J. (ed.), *Public Policy for the Seas*, MIT Press, 1970.
Williams, W. W., *Coastal Changes*, Greenwood, 1975.

Articles

Bailey, Gil, "The Coastal Plan: Battle for the Shoreline," *Cry California*, summer 1976.
Cartabruno, Leah, "Coastline Conflict: Whose Sacred Cow Will Be Eaten?" *California Journal*, August 1976.
Clark, John R. and Robb Turner, "Barrier Islands: A Threatened, Fragile Resource," *Conservation Foundation Letter*, August 1976.
Coastal Zone Management Journal, selected issues.
Johannes, Robert E., "Life and Death of the Reef," *Audubon*, September 1976.
NOAA Magazine, selected issues.
Oceans, selected issues.
Sabatier, Paul A., "Regulating Development Along the California Coast," *Journal of Soil and Water Conservation*, July-August 1976.
Schoenbaum, Thomas J. and Ronald H. Rosenberg, "The Legal Implementation of Coastal Zone Management: The North Carolina Model," *Duke Law Journal*, March 1976.
Southern California Law Review (issue devoted to California Coastal Plan), May 1976.
Tunley, Roul, "Victory in the Wetlands," *Shreveport Magazine*, November 1975.
Windom, Herbert L., "Environmental Aspects of Dredging in the Coastal Zone," *CRC Critical Reviews in Environmental Control*, March 1976.

Reports and Studies

Commission on Marine Science, Engineering and Resources, "Our Nation and the Sea," January 1969.
Congressional Research Service, "Effects of Offshore Oil and Natural Gas Development on the Coastal Zone," March 1976.
Council on Environmental Quality, "Environmental Quality—1976," September 1976.
Editorial Research Reports, "Coastal Conservation," 1970 Vol. I, p. 141; "Oceanic Law," 1974 Vol. I, p. 405; "Offshore Oil Search," 1973 Vol. II, p. 539.
Frank, Richard A., "Deepsea Mining and the Environment," The American Society of International Law, April 1976.
League of Women Voters Education Fund, "The Onshore Impact of Offshore Oil," 1976.
Office of Coastal Zone Management, selected reports and studies.

POLLUTION CONTROL: COSTS AND BENEFITS

by

John Hamer

Feb. 27
1 9 7 6

POLLUTION CONTROL:
COSTS AND BENEFITS

T HE WORDS "ecology" and "economy" come from the same etymological root—from the Greek word meaning "household management." Yet in recent years the two words have taken on conflicting connotations, with environmental protection widely labeled an enemy of economic progress. The drive to stop pollution and clean up the environment, which came to resemble a national crusade in the giddy aftermath of Earth Day 1970, ran head-on into energy shortages, rising inflation, spreading unemployment and deepening recession in the middle years of the decade. Cleaning up the environment and getting the economy back on its feet suddenly were regarded as mutually exclusive. Industry spokesmen, labor leaders and elected officials argued strongly that environmental regulations should be relaxed to stimulate the economy and preserve jobs. Pollution control and environmental improvement were branded as luxuries the nation could ill afford.

Today, however, the tide has turned again, in an unexpected direction. Evidence is mounting that pollution control not only is compatible with economic advancement but actually may contribute to it. Much of the new evidence comes from the federal environmental agencies, which clearly have a stake in promoting pollution control, but some comes from the marketplace. Investments in pollution-control programs and equipment have been found to encourage employment, increase production, create new markets and, on balance, contribute to the national economy.

A booming new pollution-control industry has sprung up to help companies and cities meet environmental standards established by federal, state and local governments. Environmental protection also has been found to benefit the economy in indirect ways—by reducing the health, recreational, agricultural and esthetic costs and damages of pollution. These "external" effects were disregarded for decades as insignificant or unavoidable, but recent calculations have shown their true economic costs to be enormous.

"The lack of adverse economic impact has been the biggest surprise in the unfolding of our programs of environmental reform," John R. Quarles Jr., deputy administrator of the Environmental Protection Agency, said recently. "Industrial extremists typically assumed the worst.... Many industries had predicted widespread plant closings and employee layoffs as a result of the new laws. In fact, the changes have been totally overshadowed by the emergence of environmental expenditures as a positive force in the economy."[1]

One of the most significant recent developments in pollution control was an "Environmental Industry Conference" held in Washington, D.C., in December 1975. Sponsored by the President's Council on Environmental Quality,[2] the conference brought together representatives of more than 200 companies and associations involved in the pollution-control business. In advance of the conference, the council asked two Wall Street analysts to examine the current status and future prospects of the pollution-control industry.

The resulting study, "The Environmental Control Industry—An Analysis of Conditions and Prospects for the Pollution Control Equipment Industry," was prepared by Kenneth Ch'uan-k'ai Leung of F. Eberstadt & Co., Inc., and Jeffrey A. Klein, an independent consultant who has worked for Kidder Peabody and Co., Inc. They reported that several hundred companies were active in pollution control. The study found that industrial, federal, state and local environmental spending, along with associated operating and maintenance expenditures, currently provides more than one million jobs in the United States. Klein and Leung concluded:

> When all factors are considered (including the impact on health and property) there does seem to be an outright economic advantage to pollution control....

A council study in April 1975 on "Environmental Programs and Employment" had similarly found that "the net impact of environmental programs on employment is positive—more people are employed as the result of environmental programs than would be without them. Environmental programs are stimulating construction, equipment and research expenditures that would not otherwise be undertaken."

Efforts to Assess Environmental Cleanup Costs

The council, in its latest annual report, estimated that $21.6-billion was spent on pollution abatement in 1974 *(see table, p. 96)*, averaging $47 per person in the United States. The council further estimated that $381-billion would be spent in the following decade, through the year 1983, doubling the per-person an-

---

[1] Quoted by the Associated Press in *The Washington Star*, Dec. 30, 1975.

[2] With the cooperation and support of the Industrial Gas Cleaning Institute, the National Solid Wastes Management Association, and the Water and Wastewater Equipment Manufacturers Association.

Pollution and the Public

Despite the cost of pollution-control programs, public support for environmental spending has remained strong. The Opinion Research Corporation of Princeton, N.J., a division of McGraw-Hill, in August 1975 released a survey on "Public Attitudes Toward Environmental Tradeoffs." It was based on phone interviews conducted in May and June 1975 with 1,222 persons age 18 and older from across the nation.

The polling organization found that "Even during a time of recession, high unemployment, and rising fuel costs, the public does not voice a readiness to cut back on environmental control programs to solve economic and energy problems." Fully 60 per cent of those surveyed felt it was more important to pay higher prices and taxes to protect the environment than to keep costs down but run the risk of more air and water pollution.

Even so, those surveyed were sharply divided on the question of environment versus employment. They were almost evenly divided—43 per cent agreed and 44 per cent disagreed—on the statement that cleaning up the environment is more important, even if it means closing down some old plants and causing some unemployment.

nual average to $98. In a chapter on "Environmental Economics," the report[3] attempted to assess the environmental costs and economic impact of pollution-control programs. It divided the environmental costs into four categories:

Damage costs—those resulting from direct pollution damages, such as blighted crops, increased illness and higher death rates.

Avoidance costs—the financial and other economic and social costs of attempting to avoid pollution, such as buying air conditioners or moving away from polluted cities.

Abatement costs—the value of resources devoted to reducing pollution, plus indirect effects of such expenditures on economic growth, employment and production.

Transaction costs—the value of resources used in the research, planning, administration, communication and monitoring of pollution control.

The report acknowledged the difficulty of obtaining precise figures, particularly on damage and avoidance costs. "It is disturbing to remain in such a state of ignorance about the various costs and benefits associated with programs to safeguard the environment. Although as a nation we are committed to large expenditures, we do not know whether we are spending too much or too little."

[3] "Environmental Quality—The Sixth Annual Report of the Council on Environmental Quality," February 1976, pp. 494-495.

The uncertainty results mainly from ignorance about pollution and its effects on people and the environment. There is uncertainty about how much pollution exists in the nation, what types of pollutants are being emitted and where, how much pollution remains in the environment, how pollutants interact, and how much actual and measurable damage occurs.

"Estimating the dollar cost of painting a pollution-soiled building or of replacing ruined crops is relatively straightforward," the council report said. "But the value of a human life or of a clear sky, or of a place for recreation...cannot be fully translated into dollars.... The fundamental decision that we shall have programs to improve environmental quality is not in question. The crucial question today is not whether to improve the environment, but how much. How much will we gain by increased expenditures, and what are the tradeoffs?"

Assigning a dollar figure to the costs and benefits of pollution control is indeed a tricky exercise. There is no widely accepted method of cost-benefit analysis. Studies done for the Environmental Protection Agency between 1966 and 1975 estimated the annual cost of air-pollution damage in the United States at anywhere from $2-billion to $35.4-billion. Most of the studies said the cost was at least $10-billion a year, however, and two of the most recent said the best estimate was around $20-billion annually. Estimates of annual water-pollution damage also vary widely, but two studies done in 1975 for the agency agreed on the cost figure—that it was about $10-billion a year. According to a draft report of the National Water Quality Commission, made public in September 1975, the cumulative benefits from cleaning up the nation's waters would amount to $12.9-billion by 1980, $36.7-billion by 1985, and $134.2-billion by the year 2000.[4]

The National Wildlife Federation since 1969 has compiled an annual "Environmental Quality Index," attempting to describe numerically the nation's environmental status in seven categories: air, water, wildlife, timber, soil, minerals and living space. According to its latest index[5] estimates:

Annual costs		**Annual costs**	
If air pollution were controlled	$14.2-billion	If water pollution were controlled	$13.2-billion
Air pollution damages	12.3-billion	Water pollution damages	11.5-billion
Net control cost	$ 1.9-billion	Net control cost	$ 1.7-billion

[4] Klein and Leung, "The Environmental Control Industry," p. 25.
[5] "The 1976 Environmental Quality Index," *National Wildlife*, February-March 1976.

All of the damage cost estimates probably are conservative, since esthetic effects, morbidity, chronic disease and mortality are difficult to evaluate monetarily. Health damage estimates may be especially low since cancer and chronic illness were not considered in most of the studies. Yet evidence is accumulating that a large proportion of cancer cases may be caused by pollutants in the environment or the workplace.

Employment Factor in Pollution-Control Spending

The precise number of jobs created by pollution-control expenditures in the United States is unknown. However, by piecing together various manpower studies by federal, state and industry groups, some general estimates have been made. The Bureau of Labor Statistics recently estimated that for each $1-billion spent on federal pollution-control programs in 1970, some 66,900 jobs were created.[6] Russell W. Peterson, chairman of the Council on Environmental Quality, told the Environmental Industry Conference in December 1975 that $15.7-billion had been spent by government and industry during the year on pollution control. He said that private industry had spent about $10-billion, the federal government around $4.2-billion, and state and local governments the remaining $1.5-billion.

Applying the Bureau of Labor Statistics' rule-of-thumb to Peterson's $15.7-billion figure, it could be surmised that about 1.1 million jobs were created in 1975 by pollution-control spending. However, the council calculates jobs-to-dollars on a different basis—roughly 85,000 jobs per billion.[7] Using that yardstick, the job figure rises to 1.3 billion. Federal laws passed since 1970 to control water and air pollution have been responsible for the creation of most of the jobs. Local governments have been aided particularly by federal funds for the construction of sewers and sewage treatment plants. This work is considered "labor intensive," requiring a relatively large number of workers.

The number of jobs lost in factories forced to close because of pollution-control laws has been far below industry predictions. A recent study by the Environmental Protection Agency's "Economic Dislocation Early Warning System" showed that only 75 plants had closed and 15,710 workers had lost their jobs in the past five years because of environmental regulations—only .016 per cent of the total labor force. Most of the plants

---

[6] The figure 66,900 is an average; the number of jobs varies by the field in which the spending occurs, as follows: 76,700 in research and development, 78,400 in abatement and control operations, 84,000 in radiation control, and 53,600 in waste-water treatment. See "Impact of Federal Pollution Control and Abatement Expenditures on Manpower Requirements," U.S. Department of Labor, Bureau of Labor Statistics, 1975.

[7] The council estimated that up to 25,000 jobs would be created at construction sites, 25,-000 in equipment manufacturing and materials processing, and 35,000 from the indirect effect of consumer spending by the new workers.

shut down were old, inefficient and marginally profitable, and probably would have closed even without anti-pollution laws, according to the report. Most of the workers promptly found jobs in nearby plants, it added.

"The problem of plant closings should not be understated, however," the Council on Environmental Quality said in its 1975 annual report. "There is some geographical concentration of the plants which have closed, and many are located in older, industrial towns already suffering relatively high unemployment rates. Their closures can seriously hurt the local economy and people who may have difficulty finding other jobs." Plant closings attributable, or partly attributable, to pollution-abatement costs have been most numerous in these industries: iron and steel (16), food products (11), paper and paper products (10), and chemicals (6).

Rise and Growth of an Environmental Industry

The other—brighter—side of the picture is the new industry that has sprung up to meet the demand for pollution-control equipment. The Klein-Leung study said the industry consisted of at least 600 companies, including more than a dozen "visibly identified" with pollution control, several divisions of larger corporations, and numerous small outfits. Profits have not grown as rapidly in recent years as in the past, Klein and Leung found, largely because of high capital requirements, intense competition, operating inexperience, manpower and materials shortages and inflation. "There are signs, however, that the industry is maturing and that profit margins are stabilizing and are likely to expand in the future," the two analysts reported. "As profits improve, industry participants should be more willing and able to commit resources for capacity expansion."

If total U.S. commitments to pollution-control programs increase, as they seem certain to do over the next decade, the industry can expect sustained growth, most analysts believe. A 1974 study of 12 companies involved in pollution control found that their average sales growth over a seven-year period was 1,775 per cent.[8] Reviewing the industry in 1975, *Barron's* business weekly predicted, "The overall market for gadgetry to clean up the environment is expected to outstrip the growth in the GNP [gross national product] for most of the next decade."[9] *Barron's* cited a study by Frost & Sullivan, a New York market research firm, which projected a 10.5 per cent average annual growth in the market for air-pollution-abatement equipment. The same study said that outlays for waste-water treatment

[8] Eileen Kohl Kaufmann, "On Fighting Pollution for Profit," *Business and Society Review*, spring 1974.
[9] David A. Loehwing, "Whiff of Recovery—Pollution Control Has Gone Back Into the Black," *Barron's*, July 14, 1975.

plants by industry and municipalities were expected to climb by about 8 per cent a year.

At the Environmental Industry Conference in December, Richard Love of the Air Pollution Control Group in Stamford, Conn., told the participants: "We've learned that all the environmental markets—air, water, solid waste—are far larger than anyone had imagined, and they also are slower to mature. The greatest opportunities still lie ahead for industry."

Of course, environmental expenditures are perceived in different ways by different industries. Those who benefit from the pollution-control market, such as environmental equipment manufacturers, may ignore the high cost to industries forced to install new controls. On the other hand, those who must comply with strict environmental regulations may consider their investment expenses as money down the drain. Moreover, some industries pollute more than others and thus must spend much more to control pollution. And then there are industries that may both benefit and suffer from strict control requirements. Cement makers, for example, probably will experience increased sales as a result of plant construction for waste-water treatment. At the same time, new cement plants require equipment to control air pollutants.

According to estimates by the Bureau of Economic Analysis in the Department of Commerce, four basic industries— nonferrous metals; pulp and paper; iron and steel; and stone, clay and glass—put more than 10 per cent of their total plant and equipment expenditures into pollution control in 1973-74, the most recent years for which figures were available. This compared to an average of 7.8 per cent for all manufacturing and 4.8 per cent for all businesses. The petroleum and chemical industries also incurred high costs, but the electric utility industry was hit hardest of all by environmental regulations.[10] The nation's utilities spent nearly $3-billion on anti-pollution measures in 1973-74, more than twice as much as the petroleum industry and nearly three times as much as the nonferrous metals industry. And these utility investments are expected to be higher than any other industry's over the next decade.

Varied Reactions of Companies to New Standards

Some companies actually have profited from their experience with controlling their own pollution. Perhaps the most notable example is Dow Chemical Co., which started early and acted aggressively to clean up its wastes. In January 1975, Dow formed a subsidiary, Hydroscience Associates, Inc., to sell its expertise in pollution control. Edwin L. Barnhart, president of the

---

[10] See "Future of Utilities," *E.R.R.*, 1975 Vol. I, pp. 185-204.

new subsidiary, has said its greatest potential growth is in making environmental assessment studies for companies. "I think there's a $100-million market for industrial-pollution control, and no one's exploited more than 10 per cent of it," Barnhart said.[11]

On the other hand, some companies have resisted cleaning up. The U.S. Steel Corp. was called the worst offender by John R. Quarles Jr., in a speech to the Conference Board in New York on Feb. 5, 1976. He said the company's poor record was giving all of industry a bad reputation. U.S. Steel's vice president for environmental affairs, Earl Mallick, said Quarles' statement was "neither factual nor truthful." Mallick said the company had invested nearly $1-billion in pollution control and would "match its environmental progress and programs with other companies and other industries."[12]

Most analyses indicate that the burden of pollution-control requirements on American industry will not be intolerable. Projected investment for environmental purposes by all U.S. industries over the 1974-83 period is unlikely to exceed 6 per cent of total plant and equipment expenditures in any one year and should average about 3 per cent over the decade, according to the Council on Environmental Quality. The council and the Environmental Protection Agency say that demands for pollution-control investments will not disrupt the nation's money markets or displace significant amounts of capital expansion funds. As for inflation, several independent analyses have shown that pollution-control spending increased the rate of inflation by less than 1 per cent a year.[13]

Although there has been some resistance on the part of business and industry to meeting the nation's environmental protection demands, there is evidence that this attitude is changing. Dr. Carl Madden, chief economist for the U.S. Chamber of Commerce, said not long ago: "In the long-range view, maybe it's best for the country if prices go up in industries that are excessive polluters and resource users. Maybe what the ecologists have shown us is that the most economic products are those that result in the least waste." If Madden's attitude spreads throughout the nation's business and industrial community, then America's pollution-control efforts almost certainly will be more successful, and much sooner than expected.

---

[11] "How Dow Sells Its Cleanup Business," *Business Week*, Jan. 20, 1975, p. 74D.

[12] Quoted in *The Wall Street Journal*, Feb. 6, 1976.

[13] The same holds true for future projections. See, for example, "The Macroeconomic Impacts of Federal Pollution Control Programs," Chase Econometric Associates, Inc., January 1975.

Problems of Water-Pollution Control

T HE PRINCIPAL federal law on water pollution is the Federal Water Pollution Control Act Amendments of 1972 (PL 92-500), the most comprehensive and expensive environmental legislation in the nation's history. This law initiated a major change in the basic approach to water-pollution control in the United States by limiting effluent discharges and setting water-quality standards. It set a national goal of eliminating all pollutant discharges into U.S. waters by 1985 and an interim goal of making the waters safe for fish, shellfish, wildlife and people by July 1, 1983. To that end, it required all U.S. industries, by July 1, 1977, to use the "best practicable control technology currently available" for treatment of any discharges. By July 1, 1983, industries will have to use the "best available technology economically achievable."

Limits are based on categories and classes of industries, and are aimed at complete elimination of discharges if technologically and economically possible. Industries may seek relief from the requirements based on alleged lack of economic capability. The law authorized more than $24.6-billion to be spent in cleaning up the nation's waters, including $18-billion in federal construction grants to the states for building waste-water treatment plants. These are allotted on the basis of need, as determined by the Environmental Protection Agency. The federal government pays 75 per cent of the costs and state and local governments provide the remaining 25 per cent. Finally, a pollutant-discharge-permit program was established under strict guidelines administered by the agency.

More than three years after the law's enactment, there is serious question about whether its goals are too ambitious. There are conflicting indications as to how well the requirements are being met by government and industry. On the one hand, the Environmental Protection Agency admits that some 9,000 communities serving 60 per cent of the nation's population will not be able to meet the first-stage deadlines for sewage cleanup. The agency has issued about 26,000 industrial permits for dumping limited amounts of wastes into the nation's waterways, but spot checks showed two out of three permit holders were in violation, according to the National Wildlife Federation. On the other hand, about 5,000 new waste-water treatment plants currently are under construction, and federal grants to cities are rising sharply. In a speech last fall to the Water Pollution Control Federation, EPA Administrator

Estimates of Pollution-Abatement Expenditures

(in billions of dollars)

Pollutant	1974	1983	1974-83 Cumulative
Air Pollution			
Public	0.2	0.8	6.0
Private			
Mobile	5.1	8.8	70.2
Industrial	1.8	8.4	55.6
Utilities	1.0	5.9	34.3
Total Air Pollution	8.1	23.9	166.1
Water Pollution			
Public			
Federal	0.2	0.2	2.3
State and local	7.2	12.6	97.8
Private			
Industrial	2.3	11.2	57.1
Utilities	0.2	1.3	8.1
Total Water Pollution	9.9	25.3	165.3
Solid Waste			
Public	1.5	2.7	21.3
Private	2.1	3.4	28.1
Total Solid Waste	3.6	6.1	49.4
Radiation			
Nuclear Power Plants	—	0.05	0.2
Grand Total	21.6	55.3	381.0

No estimates available for strip-mined land reclamation and noise control.

SOURCE: Council on Environmental Quality

Russell E. Train said: "Over 97 per cent of all water dischargers are either now in compliance with pollution-control standards or are on definite water cleanup schedules...."[14]

One of the biggest problems with the program involved the $18-billion authorized for construction of sewage treatment plants. In 1972, the Nixon administration impounded most of this money, and only when the Supreme Court early in 1975 ruled the impoundment illegal was a substantial amount released to states and localities. These grants fell from $1.6-billion in 1973 to $1.4-billion in 1974, then jumped to $3.6-billion in 1975 and are expected to climb to $5.2-billion in 1976 and $6.2-billion in 1977.

---

[14] Speech in Miami Beach, Fla., Oct. 8, 1975.

Another provision of the 1972 act established a 15-member National Commission on Water Quality to investigate the problems of achieving the 1983 goals and to report to Congress and the nation. That group's final report is due to be published later in 1976. A draft report made public in the fall of 1975 said that cleaning up the nation's lakes and rivers would cost industry and government between $97-billion and $130-billion by 1983, considerably lower than the Council on Environmental Quality's estimate of $165-billion.

The draft report said that such a cleanup would result in higher prices for many consumer items and would cause some unemployment and some factory shutdowns. But it said the benefits of such expenditures would include substantial improvements in commercial and recreational fishing, wider availability of beaches and swimming areas, and increased property values for land near water. The economic benefits from opening more beaches and improving fishing would total more than $27-billion by 1985, the report said. The draft report did not mention health aspects of water pollution. If health factors were included, the potential benefits of water cleanup expenditures would be much higher. A staff estimate put the cost of water cleanup at $44 per person a year for the next 10 years.

Shortly after the draft report was made public, a White House task force sharply criticized the work of the National Water Quality Commission in another report. The task force, a part of the Domestic Council, said the commission had underestimated costs and overestimated benefits in its draft. However, several commission staff members said the White House task force was biased in favor of industry, pointing out that 11 of its 26 members were from the Department of Commerce while only 5 were from environmental agencies.[15]

Pollution From Farms, Mines and Construction

Even so, there have been other suggestions that some of the costs of water cleanup are being underestimated. In an analysis in *Power Engineering* magazine, F. C. Olds said government figures showing total cleanup costs over the next decade to be more than $300-billion do not include "costs to cope with acid mine drainage, agricultural feed lot runoff, urban storm water runoff problems, noise levels, the ultimate zero discharge, and numerous other matters relating to environmental protection." He called the present laws "unworkable" and "unrealistic."[16]

Some government environmental officials also see enforcement difficulty ahead. Gary Dietrich of the Office of Water and

[15] *The Washington Star*, Oct. 10, 1975.
[16] "Environmental Cleanup 1975-1985: Huge New Costs, Little Benefit," *Power Engineering*, September 1975, p. 38.

Hazardous Materials has said: "We are in the finishing stages of the first round of our battle against water pollution. The second round will be far more difficult because we will be dealing with toxic pollutants which we know little about."[17] The Environmental Protection Agency has found excessive levels of toxic heavy metals such as mercury, cadmium, manganese, lead and iron in most major American river systems. They have concluded that "non-point" sources—rainwater, storm sewers, and agricultural runoff—are responsible for much of this contamination. The Council on Environmental Quality has estimated that it would cost $235-billion to control storm-sewer runoff alone—nearly half again as much as the projected expenditures for all other types of water-pollution control during the 1974-83 decade.

Train, in his speech to the Water Pollution Control Federation, pointed out that more than 400 million acres in the nation are crop land, from which two billion tons of sediment flow annually into lakes and streams. This includes much of the 440 million pounds of toxic pesticides used every year, as well as nitrogen and phosphorus from the 41 million tons of fertilizers used every year. In addition, enormous quantities of animal wastes enter the nation's waters. Livestock produce 10 times more waste than do humans. Five to 10 per cent of the total sediment load in the nation's rivers comes from the 10 to 12 million acres of commercial forest harvested every year.[18]

Strip mining is another source of pollutants, affecting some 350,000 acres annually. In northern Appalachia alone, mine drainage discharges more than one million metric tons of acid into surface and ground waters every day.[19] Construction and excavation related to urban sprawl, which consumes hundreds of square miles per year, generate even more sediment than agricultural activities. Congress placed primary responsibility for the management of "non-point" source pollution with the states, and there is considerable variation in the efficacy of state programs.

Mixed Results From Air-Pollution Fight

THE ORIGINAL deadline for cleaning up the nation's air, under the Clean Air Act of 1970, was May 31, 1975. By that date, the air was supposed to be "safe enough to protect the public's health." Just before the deadline, Train confessed: "Despite significant progress, a number of the nation's 247 air-

---

[17] "A Turn in the Tide—Pollution Battle Being Won?" *U.S. News & World Report*, Aug. 4, 1975, p. 57.
[18] See "Forest Policy," *E.R.R.*, 1975 Vol. II, pp. 865-884.
[19] See "Strip Mining," *E.R.R.*, 1973 Vol. II, pp. 861-881.

quality-control regions will not meet all of the air quality standards." In two out of every three regions, pollution levels were higher than those specified by the 1970 act.

However, the air in most U.S. cities today is considerably cleaner than it was five years ago, even if it does not meet the strict standards of the act. Concentrations of sulfur dioxide have dropped 25 per cent nationwide since 1970, including a 50 per cent decrease in major metropolitan areas, according to the Environmental Protection Agency. Particulate matter—dust, smoke and soot—has decreased by 14 per cent nationally over the same period. Automobile exhaust pollution from 1975 model cars was as much as 80 per cent below that from 1967 cars of comparable weight and engine size. Still, auto emissions remain one of the largest sources of urban air pollution today.

Why the mixed results in fighting air pollution? "No one back in December of 1970 imagined that it would be easy to achieve clean air," Train has said. "However, many of us doubtless underestimated the complexities involved, and certainly few foresaw...the worldwide energy crisis and economic recession."[20] States are hampered by lack of funds to hire inspectors to enforce the laws. Even so, both the Environmental Protection Agency and the Council on Environmental Quality are continuing to push the message that the costs of cleaning up the nation's air are well worth the benefits that will be derived.

The National Academy of Sciences has estimated that air pollution causes 15,000 deaths and seven million sick days a year. The EPA has estimated that medical costs, plus lost working days, could total as much as $7.6-billion a year. In addition, air pollution damages property, clothing and other materials. The agency said pollution causes urban families to pay up to $57 a year to clean and replace soiled clothes and $20 a year to repaint houses and automobiles. In the past, air pollution was not a significant problem in rural areas, but that may be changing. In 1975, the agency said that dangerous levels of smog had been detected in broad regions of the eastern United States. In some instances, pollution levels were worse in communities 50 miles beyond major cities than in the cities themselves. Sometimes this is attributable to heavy commuting traffic and sometimes to electric power plant smokestacks.

Deadlines for Auto Emissions, Stationary Sources

Deadlines for the final standards on three automobile exhaust pollutants—carbon monoxide, hydrocarbons and nitrogen oxides—have been delayed three times and are now set to take effect for 1978 model cars. Most American manufacturers have

---

[20] Quoted in *U.S. News & World Report,* Aug. 4, 1975, p. 58.

turned to the catalytic converter to clean up exhausts, but under some conditions these devices have produced sulfuric acid mist—another potentially dangerous pollutant.[21] President Ford has asked Congress to delay the imposition of the original emission standards and to keep the present levels in effect through the 1981 model year. In the Senate, a bill was reported by the Public Works Committee early in February 1976 to grant a one-year delay, until 1979, for automakers to meet the carbon monoxide and hydrocarbon standards.

As for stationary sources of air pollution, such as industrial smokestacks and electric power plants, the big fight has been over the installation of "scrubbers" to remove hazardous pollutants from emissions. The Environmental Protection Agency has said that of 220,000 stationary sources of noxious fumes in this country, 20,000 account for 85 per cent of the emissions. The agency is concentrating on these primary polluters and has investigated most of them, achieving compliance from more than 80 per cent. However, some 3,000 major polluters still are in violation of the law, and a concerted effort to clean up their pollution is now under way. Electric utilities have been pushing for adoption of emission standards that could be met by the construction of tall smokestacks (to disperse pollutants over a wide area), and by use of so-called "intermittent" standards, which entail closing down plants only when an atmospheric inversion or other weather condition creates a pollution hazard.

The EPA, however, is insisting on the installation of scrubbers, which it claims have been operating reliably for a year or more at several places around the nation. About 100 power plants already are committed to scrubbers despite the high cost of installation but 150 to 200 others have resisted scrubber technology. The Industrial Gas Cleaning Institute, which represents scrubber manufacturers, estimates that scrubbers cost about half as much as the measurable damages caused every year by the fumes they would eliminate. The Senate Public Works Committee bill would require utilities and factories to meet compliance schedules, although those under order to burn coal because of oil shortages could receive extensions.

Congressional Proposal to Aid Urban Compliance

As for general air-quality standards in the nation's cities, the initial goal of the 1970 act has been found unrealistic. At least 30 major cities still would have polluted air even if they met all automobile, industry and utility standards. These cities would have to take more drastic measures—such as restricting traffic

---

[21] See "Auto Emission Controls," *E.R.R.*, 1973 Vol. I, pp. 289-312.

or shortening work weeks—to bring their air-pollution levels into compliance. But even though many Americans express general support for limiting cars in downtown areas, improving mass transit, encouraging car pools and establishing exclusive bus lanes, most individuals remain resistant to changing their driving habits. The proposed Senate bill would allow cities up to 10 extra years to meet the 1977 compliance deadline, provided they adopted "reasonable transportation control measures" such as bus lanes and car inspection programs.

Another major issue in the air-pollution fight is that of "nondegradation"—the concept that air quality should not be allowed to deteriorate in sparsely populated areas where it is already cleaner than the law requires. As more and more regions are viewed as desirable for development, this will be a growing controversy. Environmentalists argue that the air should be kept as pure as it now is in such areas, while developers contend that the air should be permitted to reach a pollution level comparable to that in other populated areas. The Senate bill would allow states to set up a classification system for non-polluted areas, with strict standards for national parks, wilderness areas and other pristine regions, and lesser standards elsewhere.

The bill also would set up a procedure to protect workers against "environmental blackmail"—getting laid off or fired by employers who blame the cost of meeting clean air standards—by allowing them to demand a hearing before the Secretary of Labor. The EPA also would be able to hold public hearings on plant closings that are attributed to the cost of compliance with federal air-pollution-control regulations. The House is far behind the Senate in its consideration of Clean Air Act amendments, but it is expected to deal with many of the same issues in its version of the legislation.[22]

Questions of Solid Waste and Land Use

O FTEN IGNORED in analyses of the costs and benefits of pollution control are the problems of solid waste and land use, both of which are enormously complicated issues and are intertwined with air and water pollution. More than 135 million tons of solid wastes are generated by America's households, stores and office buildings annually—about 1,000 pounds a year for every man, woman and child—and the amount is growing by 3 to 4 per cent a year. If agricultural, industrial, construction,

---

[22] See *Congressional Quarterly Weekly Report*, Feb. 14, 1976, p. 311.

Capital Investments for Pollution Control

(in billions)

	1968	1970	1972	1974
Total Capital Investments	$67.77	$79.71	$88.44	$112.40
Pollution-Control Investments	1.13	2.50	4.50	6.92
Per Cent of Total	1.7%	3.1%	5.1%	6.2%

SOURCE: McGraw-Hill Publications Company

sewage and mining wastes are included, the total exceeds 4.5 billion tons a year. The amount of solid waste discarded per person in the United States has doubled in the past 50 years, and is growing about five times faster than the population.[23]

This solid waste is such a problem because traditional means of refuse disposal cannot keep up with the burgeoning amounts of garbage and trash. About half of the nation's cities are running out of available land for waste disposal, according to a 1974 survey by the National League of Cities. Open city dumps are being closed by the Environmental Protection Agency because they create air pollution when trash is burned, water pollution when it rains, and other health and esthetic damage. Sanitary landfill is an alternative used by about 80 per cent of the nation's cities, but relatively few operate within accepted standards, which require that garbage and trash be compacted and covered with a layer of earth by bulldozers or dump trucks each day. No burning is allowed.

Development of Resource Recovery Technology

Large-scale resource recovery is being touted by many leaders of industry, science and government as the best answer to the solid-waste crisis. Garbage is collected by trucks in the normal manner, then ground up in a shredder and run through a magnetic separator which removes metals that can be recycled by steel mills. Glass and other materials also may be removed for recycling. The remaining shredded trash is mixed with coal or other fuels and can be burned to produce steam in electric power plants.

About 50 cities today are in some stage of commitment to resource or energy recovery, although only a few systems actually are operating or under construction. Some have been criticized for high air-pollution levels. The new technology shows promise, but the cost of building recovery facilities is high, and most of the plants built so far have relied on subsidies.

---

[23] See "Solid Waste Technology," *E.R.R.*, 1974 Vol. II, pp. 641-660.

Making them self-supporting is difficult because the market for scrap materials is cyclical. Some analysts believe that "source reduction"—cutting down on excess packaging and eliminating throwaway containers—is preferable to building elaborate resource-recovery plants and would be less costly.

Another difficult land-pollution problem is sludge, the mucky residue of sewage treatment. Until recently, sludge usually was burned or buried, or dumped into bays or oceans. But today, because of population expansion and improved sewage treatment, there is much more sludge around. And stiffer environmental standards are making it harder to dispose of. "Sludge is the most serious dilemma we face in waste-water treatment," an EPA official has said.[24] "It's Catch-22. The cleaner we make the water, the more sludge we create." Sludge often contains toxic materials such as heavy metals and pesticides, as well. Nationally, about four million tons of sludge are generated annually, and that total is expected to reach 10 million tons by 1985. Cities are experimenting with a variety of disposal methods, such as converting sludge to methane gas, burning it under pressure, and dumping it on crop lands as fertilizer. But there are problems with all of these methods, and the search continues for an environmentally and economically sound solution.

Issues of Land Use Planning and Urban Sprawl

Air pollution, water pollution, solid waste and sludge pollution are all related closely to the way the United States uses its land. Land use is the realm in which all other forms of pollution come together, for without careful land-use planning, effective pollution control is difficult if not impossible to achieve. Urban sprawl, for example, almost always generates air, water and solid waste pollution, while unplanned development in rural areas can do the same thing. Congress, after repeated attempts, has not passed a comprehensive national land-use planning bill, although 17 states enacted land-use laws in 1975.

The land-use issue exemplifies the entire range of arguments over pollution control. The perception of costs and benefits varies among different people. While some believe that environmental protection must take precedence, others insist that economic considerations should hold sway. Polarization between the two extremes is quick to develop, with the result that the controversy breaks down into a hopeless battle of true believers. What the new analyses of environmental economics are indicating, however, is that there is no need for the nation to choose between a clean environment *or* a healthy economy. It should be possible for the United States to have both.

---

[24] Unidentified official quoted in *The Wall Street Journal*, Dec. 16, 1975.

Selected Bibliography

Books

Auld, D. A. L. (ed.), *Economic Thinking and Pollution Problems*, University of Toronto Press, 1972.

Baxter, William F., *People or Penguins—The Case for Optimal Pollution*, Columbia University Press, 1974.

Goldman, Marshall I. (ed.), *Controlling Pollution—The Economics of a Cleaner America*, Prentice-Hall, 1967.

Kneese, Allen V. and Charles L. Schultze, *Pollution, Prices, and Public Policy*, Brookings Institution, 1975.

Kneese, Allen V., Robert U. Ayres, and Ralph C. d'Arge, *Economics and the Environment: A Materials Balance Approach*, Johns Hopkins University Press, 1970.

Articles

"EPA Aims to Preserve Profits While Protecting Environment," *Commerce Today*, Nov. 24, 1975.

Heffernan, Patrick, "Jobs and the Environment," *Sierra Club Bulletin*, April 1975.

Loehwing, David A., "Whiff of Recovery—Pollution Control Has Gone Back Into the Black," *Barron's*, July 14, 1975.

McWethy, Jack, "Now, Second Thoughts About Cleaning Up the Environment," *U.S. News & World Report*, Jan. 19, 1976.

National Wildlife, selected issues containing annual Environmental Quality Index.

Olds, F. C., "Environmental Cleanup 1975-1985: Huge New Costs, Little Benefit," *Power Engineering*, September 1975.

"The Surprisingly High Cost of a Safer Environment," *Business Week*, Sept. 14, 1974.

Studies and Reports

Abel, Fred H., Dennis P. Tihansky and Richard G. Walsh, "National Benefits of Water Pollution Control," Environmental Protection Agency, 1975.

Biniek, Joseph P., "The Status of Environmental Economics," report by the Environmental Policy Division, Congressional Research Service, Library of Congress, for the Senate Public Works Committee, June 1975.

Council on Environmental Quality, "Environmental Quality—1975," sixth annual report and selected previous reports.

—"The Economic Impact of Environmental Programs," November 1974.

—"The Macroeconomic Impacts of Federal Pollution Control Programs," January 1975.

Environmental Protection Agency, "Evaluation of Techniques for Cost Benefit Analysis of Water Pollution Control Programs and Policies," December 1974.

Leung, Kenneth Ch'uan-k'ai and Jeffrey A. Klein, "The Environmental Control Industry—An Analysis of Conditions and Prospects for the Pollution Control Equipment Industry," December 1975.

Opinion Research Corporation, "Public Attitudes Toward Environmental Tradeoffs," August 1975.

Real Estate Research Corporation, "The Costs of Sprawl—Detailed Cost Analysis," April 1974.

Waddell, T. E., "The Economic Damages of Air Pollution," Environmental Protection Agency, 1974.

FOREST POLICY

by

John Hamer

**Nov. 28
1975**

FOREST POLICY

A MERICA'S FORESTS are today the subject of a bitter debate that seems certain to intensify in the months ahead. At issue are broad and complex questions about forest management: How much timber should be harvested, and where? How should trees be logged? How much forest land should be preserved for wilderness, wildlife and watershed? How can various recreation demands be reconciled? Can the forests be managed to satisfy all these needs? At stake in this debate are not only future timber supply and national housing demands *(see box, p. 113)*, but the very future of the nation's forests.

With the increase in public concern over the environment in the past few years, America's forests have aroused widespread attention and controversy. Demands on the forests are growing—and are often competing. The timber industry fights with wilderness preservationists; hikers and backpackers battle with trail-bike riders and off-road vehicle drivers; defenders of wildlife contend with hunters and fishermen; second-home developers argue with land-use planners. All of these groups want to ensure that future forest policies protect their interests.

Meanwhile, public demand for lumber, paper and other forest products, which was relatively stable for much of this century, is increasing rapidly. Between 1942 and 1972, U.S. consumption of timber for industrial wood products such as lumber, plywood and wood pulp went up 56 per cent to 13.7 billion cubic feet.[1] By the year 2000, according to U.S. Forest Service estimates, demand for timber products will almost double to reach an annual level of some 23 billion cubic feet. Based on current forest policies, timber production by the end of the century could fall short of demand by between 2.5 billion and 8.1 billion board feet.[2]

"At present, annual growth of timber in the United States exceeds cutting," Russell W. Peterson, chairman of the President's

---

[1] "The Outlook for Timber in the United States," U.S. Department of Agriculture, Forest Service, Forest Resource Report No. 20, July 1974, p. 1.
[2] A board foot is the amount of timber equal to a piece of wood 12 inches square and 1 inch thick. A cubic foot is thus 12 board feet. A typical single-family home requires 12,000 board feet of lumber and 5,000 square feet of plywood. In 1972, about 36 million board feet were used in housing and construction in the United States.

Council on Environmental Quality, said in a recent speech,[3] "but that surplus condition won't last long. Within two decades or so, projected demand for forest products will outrun harvest, both on privately owned timber land and on the publicly owned lands managed by the Forest Service."

Forests occupy 754 million acres in the 50 states, or almost 33 per cent of the nation's land area. About 500 million acres, or some 66 per cent of the forested lands, are classified as "commercial forests." These are defined as "those on sites whose stable soils, favorable climatic environment, and location favor the continuing production of large volumes of high quality timber as a dominant land use."[4] Of the 500 million acres, the federal government controls only about 107 million, or 22 per cent. This includes commercial forest lands in the national forest system, forests managed by the Bureau of Indian Affairs and the Bureau of Land Management, and other federal lands. State and other public forests occupy an additional 30 million acres, or 6 per cent. The timber industry controls some 67 million acres, or 13 per cent. But by far the largest amount of commercial forest is in the hands of small, private land owners—296 million acres, or 59 per cent—is owned by more than four million individuals in plots averaging less than 100 acres each.

The productivity of the various categories of commercial forests varies greatly. Industry-owned lands produce about 26 per cent of the timber used for wood products every year. These lands are the most intensively managed. The American Forest Institute reports that industrial forest lands average about 52 cubic feet of new wood growth per acre per year, far more than the 32 cubic feet on public forest lands. Other private forests are the least productive commercially. Their owners are often more interested in recreational, esthetic or other forest values.

The current debate over America's forests is focused primarily on the national forests, however. They contain about half of the nation's standing softwood timber—such as fir, pine, cedar, hemlock and redwood—which provides most of the lumber and plywood for housing and construction. Hardwoods—such as maple, oak, walnut, ash, hickory and birch—are found mainly on private lands and are used for furniture, flooring, paneling, pallets, and other wood products. The timber industry argues that harvesting of national forests must be increased to meet future needs. Other interest groups contend that the industry

---

[3] "Management or Gamble? The Need for Caution on Public Forests," address to the Sixth American Forest Congress, American Forestry Association, Washington, D.C., Oct. 7, 1975.
[4] "What the Forest Service Does," U.S. Department of Agriculture, Forest Service brochure, April 1975, p. 9.

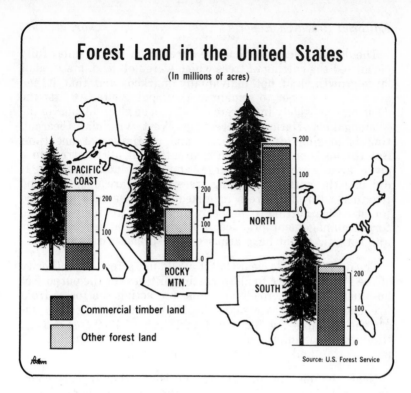

Forest Land in the United States
(In millions of acres)

PACIFIC COAST 200 100 0

ROCKY MTN. 200 100 0

NORTH 200 100 0

SOUTH 200 100 0

■ Commercial timber land

☐ Other forest land

Source: U.S. Forest Service

has already overcut its own lands and would do the same thing on public lands.

Uncertain Effect of the Monongahela Decision

The recent development that has done the most to throw the question of national forest management into a state of turmoil is the so-called "Monongahela decision" issued by the U.S. Fourth Circuit Court of Appeals in Richmond, Va., in August 1975.[5] The appeals court upheld a lower court decision which found that the Forest Service had ignored the language of its basic charter, the Organic Act of 1897 *(see p. 116)*. Environmental groups contended that three proposed timber sales violated the sales provisions of the 1897 law, which state:

> For the purpose of preserving the living and growing timber and promoting the younger growth on national forests, the Secretary of Agriculture...may cause to be designated and appraised so much of the dead, matured or large growth of trees found upon such national forests as may be compatible with the utilization of the forests thereon, and may sell the same.... Such timber, before being sold, shall be marked and designated....

[5] West Virginia Division of the Izaak Walton League of America, Sierra Club, Natural Resources Defense Council, Inc., The West Virginia Highlands Conservancy, and Forest Armentrout v. Earl L. Butz, Secretary of Agriculture; John R. McGuire, Chief of the U.S. Forest Service; Jay H. Cravens, regional forester; and Alfred H. Troutt, forest supervisor, Monongahela National Forest; No. 74-1387, appeal from the U.S. District Court for the northern district of West Virginia, at Elkins; argued Dec. 4, 1974, and decided Aug. 21, 1975.

The decision declared that the Forest Service had unlawfully permitted the cutting of trees which were not dead, matured or large-growth, and not individually marked, and that it had allowed cut timber to remain at the logging site. At first the decision was widely interpreted as a "ban on clearcutting" in the Monongahela National Forest in West Virginia. Clearcutting is logging off an entire stand of timber at one time. But the decision did not ban clearcutting if all the trees in a given area were mature, large, and individually marked. It did ban the cutting of young trees, which are usually found together with older trees in mixed-growth eastern hardwood forests. Clearcutting, if properly applied, is a widely accepted forest management practice. But abuses that led to erosion and esthetic blight have aroused widespread criticism.

The decision made clear that it would not affect the authority of the Forest Service to allow cutting of trees for the purpose of building highways, roads or trails; protecting the forest from fire, insects and disease; managing the forests for other uses under the Multiple Use-Sustained Yield Act of 1960 *(see p. 118);* thinning and improving the forests; or investigating, experimenting and testing reforestation methods.

Near the end of its 29-page decision, the appeals court declared: "We are not insensitive to the fact that our reading of the Organic Act will have serious and far-reaching consequences, and it may well be that this legislation enacted over 75 years ago is an anachronism which no longer serves the public interest. However, the appropriate forum to resolve this complex and controversial issue is not the courts but the Congress."

A week after the decision was handed down, the Forest Service suspended most timber sales from national forests in the states served by the appeals court—Virginia, West Virginia, North Carolina and South Carolina—until the agency decided whether to appeal the decision to the Supreme Court or to seek new legislation. The Forest Service on Nov. 19, 1975, asked for a 30-day extension of its deadline for appealing to the High Court through the U.S. Solicitor General in the Justice Department. An appeal would allow timber sales to continue in the four states affected, but it could lead to a rash of similar suits or requests for injunctions by environmental groups around the nation. John R. McGuire, Chief of the Forest Service, has said that if the decision were expanded to include all national forests, timber sales for the year ahead might be reduced by as much as three-fourths.

But neither the immediate nor ultimate effects of the Monongahela decision are fully known as yet. Environmental groups criticized the Forest Service's suspension of timber sales as an effort to arouse a backlash. "This move appears to have been a hasty one designed to generate adverse response to the decision," wrote Brock Evans and Gordon Robinson of the Sierra Club.[6] And Tom Barlow of the Natural Resources Defense Council said in an interview that the decision could not be implemented promptly nationwide because it would take months or even years for other cases to come to trial. "Industry cites this as a way to produce a timber crisis," Barlow charged. "But there's no real emergency here, that's just a scare threat."

Timber industry spokesmen insist that the threat is real. "We're scared out of our wits," said Warren Rogers of the National Forest Products Association (NFPA). And John B. Crowell Jr., general manager of Louisiana-Pacific Corp., a major timber company, said the decision "sets a precedent for similar actions" with a potentially drastic impact on the nation's housing market.[7] The NFPA has estimated that as many as 75,000 jobs could be lost in the wood products industry if the decision took effect nationwide. "It's a diverse industry and we can seldom get together on anything," Rogers commented. "This decision may be a unifying force."

In another recent development, the Southern Appalachian Multiple Use Council, a group formed in the aftermath of the Monongahela decision by timber interests, filed suit against Chief McGuire, challenging his authority to apply the decision to the entire four-state area.[8] The suit also argues that if the decision is applied in that area, it must be applied nationwide under equal-protection-of-the-law provisions of the Fifth and Fourteenth Amendments. The plaintiffs are seeking a temporary injunction against McGuire's administrative action which halted nearly all timber sales.

Prospects of Federal Legislation on Forestry

Those on all sides of the controversy seem to agree that the impasse will have to be solved by Congress, although there is great disagreement over the form that federal legislation should take. The industry favors some kind of "interim" bill that would allow timber sales from national forests to continue as they have in the past while a longer-term solution is worked out. Environmentalists and some members of Congress prefer to start work now on a "comprehensive" bill that would set forth

---

[6] "The Beautiful, Incredible Monongahela Decision," *Sierra Club Bulletin*, October 1975, p. 22.
[7] "The Monongahela Decision: A Crisis in Forest Management," speech to National Forest Products Association meeting, Montreal, Canada, Oct. 7, 1975.
[8] Southern Appalachian Multiple Use Council, Inc. *v.* Earl L. Butz, Secretary of Agriculture; John R. McGuire, Chief of the U.S. Forest Service; Roy Bond, regional forester; and Robert Sermack, national forest supervisor in North Carolina; civil action filed Nov. 12, 1975.

strict guidelines on timber management in the national forests. "If there were an interim bill, we'd insist that it be so onerous to the industry that it would be in their interest to come back to the bargaining table soon," said Tom Barlow.

But the industry, the Forest Service, many professional foresters and other members of Congress contend that it would be a serious mistake to try to regulate forestry by federal law. They say that no law could specify adequately what practices could or could not be used everywhere. "We would be trying to put into law the professional criteria which may vary from specie to specie and from region to region," Sen. Mark O. Hatfield (R Ore.) has said.[9]

Since the Monongahela decision, Rep. Roy A. Taylor (D N.C.) has introduced an interim measure (HR 10364) which would allow the Secretary of Agriculture, through the Forest Service, to continue selling national forest timber. The legislation would expire on Sept. 30, 1977, to give Congress a timetable for developing more comprehensive legislation. Sen. Hubert H. Humphrey (D Minn.) has circulated the draft of another interim measure which he may introduce as a "talking point." Both the Humphrey and Taylor proposals are unacceptable to environmentalists, who call this approach a "quick fix" allowing what they regard as abusive forest practices to continue. They are backing a draft bill by Sen. Jennings Randolph (D W.Va.) which represents a more comprehensive approach. The proposed bill sets forth detailed definitions and specific practices to regulate timber harvesting from the national forests—especially eastern hardwood forests—including tight restrictions on clearcutting. But the timber industry is adamantly opposed.

Forest Service Deadline on Resource Planning

Many people on both sides of the controversy believe the Monongahela decision and the forthcoming fight in Congress could have a salutary effect. "Within the next year or so the whole question of timber supply will have to be settled," said Warren Rogers of the NFPA. "If not in 1976, then by 1977, there must be a resolution of the problem of use of the forests." Similarly, Brock Evans commented: "Maybe this is the opportunity we've been looking for for years to have a full debate on the national forests and what the policies should be."

One thing certain to stimulate such a debate is the Dec. 31, 1975, deadline of the Forest and Rangeland Renewable Resources Planning Act of 1974 (PL 93-378), a far-reaching measure which was passed by Congress with little public notice. It is usually referred to as the RPA, for Resources Planning Act,

---

[9] Quoted by A. Robert Smith in the *Willamette Week*, Portland, Ore., Oct. 27, 1975.

Timber and Housing

The timber industry and the housing market are closely related. Residential construction accounts for about 50 per cent of U.S. softwood lumber and plywood consumption and 35 per cent of all wood products consumption including siding, paneling, doors, trim, windows and flooring. The housing market is currently depressed—there will be only about 1.2 million new housing starts in 1975, compared to the record 2.4 million new units built in 1972.

In the Housing and Urban Development Act of 1968, Congress set a national goal of 26 million housing units to be built or rehabilitated by 1978. The nation is nowhere near that figure today. Many critics said it was an unrealistic goal anyway—at an average of four inhabitants per unit, nearly half of the nation's population would be living in a new or renovated home by 1978.

If the housing market picks up next year as part of a general economic recovery, the cost of construction materials is expected to spurt upward. Timber industry officials predict price increases of 20 to 30 per cent at mills in the Northwest, which provide 75 per cent of the nation's construction lumber. These increases would be reflected in the cost of housing, as lumber and plywood alone represent almost 20 per cent of the selling price of a single-family dwelling.

The use of substitute materials such as aluminum, brick, concrete and plastics for housing is on the rise, but they all have greater energy and environmental costs than wood, and are made from non-renewable resources.

---

or the Humphrey-Rarick Act for its main sponsors, Sen. Hubert H. Humphrey (D Minn.) and Rep. John R. Rarick (D La., 1967-1974). The act requires the Forest Service to produce a comprehensive framework for planning the use of forest and range land. The measure applies to 750 million acres of forest lands and 600 million acres of range and grass lands—almost two-thirds of the total 2.3 billion acres of land in the United States.

Specifically, the act requires the Forest Service to prepare a "Renewable Resource Assessment" covering the present and potential supply of forest and range resources in the nation and a projection of future needs. The assessment must include all public and private forest and range lands. In addition, the agency must submit a "Renewable Resource Program" for the protection, management and development of the national forest system. It must include an inventory of specific needs, benefits, priorities, costs and personnel requirements. Then on the day Congress convenes in 1976, the President must submit to the House and Senate the assessment and the program, together with a detailed policy statement to be used in framing administration budget requests for Forest Service activities. The President is required to seek and to allocate the full amount necessary to implement the program each year—or to tell Congress why he is seeking a lesser amount.

Draft versions of the assessment and program, along with a summary, were released by the Forest Service in August 1975 for public comment. The three volumes, which total more than 1,100 pages, present a wide range of suggestions rather than specific recommendations. But the agency must come up with recommendations to send to the White House by the end of the year, and probably will submit a draft of proposed comprehensive legislation at the same time.

Almost everyone familiar with the Forest Service's activities is optimistic that the RPA will produce significant results. Gene Berghoffen, who directed the agency's response to the law, said in an interview: "We're in the business of asking what kind of future do we want, which is never an easy task. But we're starting with some national goals and objectives, and our recommended program will make some specific suggestions." William Towell of the American Forestry Association, who played a major role in formulating the Resources Planning Act and pressing for its enactment, said: "It could be the most important forestry legislation in the nation's history if it is fully implemented. This is the first time in law that the Forest Service has been told to plan for all the nation's forests, not just public or state lands."

Use and Protection of Timber Reserves

TO THE SETTLERS, the forests were an obstacle to be cleared for farms and towns. About 70 per cent of America's land—more than one billion acres—was originally covered by forests. But by the end of the 19th century it was estimated that only 500 million acres of productive forest land remained.[10] Much of the rest had been damaged by wasteful logging and careless fires. Most people still considered the timber supply to be inexhaustible. The general policy of the federal government during most of the nation's first century was to dispose of as much of the public domain as possible.[11]

---

[10] "Report Upon Forestry Investigations," Department of Agriculture, 1877-1898, H. Doc. Vol. 71, No. 181, 55th Congress (1897-1899), 2d. Session, pp. 46-47.
[11] See "Protection of the Countryside," *E.R.R.*, 1971 Vol. II, pp. 549-556.

There were some early efforts at conservation, such as William Penn's 1681 law that one acre of forest in every five should be preserved. The newly formed United States government set aside some reserves in Florida to protect stands of red oak and cedar for Navy ship-building, but these naval reserves were often invaded by private timber operators. On private lands, exploitation of the forests was a widely accepted practice. "A long history and tradition of exploitation of private forest land, with little or no concern for the future was characterized as 'cut out and get out,'" wrote Edward P. Cliff, former Chief of the U.S. Forest Service.[12]

"Simply stated, foresters have trouble seeing the forest for the timber."

Edward C. Crafts, former deputy chief,
U.S. Forest Service

A growing public awareness of the need for some conservation arose in the late 1800s, however. In 1872, after an extensive public-interest lobbying effort, Congress passed and President Grant signed a bill creating Yellowstone National Park.[13] And in 1876, in a little-noticed rider to an appropriations bill, Congress authorized the Commissioner of Agriculture to hire someone to investigate "the annual amount of consumption, importation, and exportation of timber and other forest products, the probable supply for future wants, the best means adapted to their preservation and renewal, the influence of forests upon climate, and...measures...for the preservation and restoration or planting of forests."[14]

But Congress remained ambivalent toward the conservation concept. The Timber and Stone Act of 1878 provided for the sale of 160-acre tracts of western timber lands to private individuals for $2.50 an acre, giving large timber operators the chance to acquire huge amounts. But in 1890 three more national parks were created—Yosemite, Sequoia and General Grant (which became part of King's Canyon in 1940). And the following year, in an obscure provision added to another public land law, Congress laid the foundation for more complete protection of the nation's forests. It said that "the President of the United States may, from time to time, set apart and reserve, in any state or terri-

---

[12] In "Timber: The Renewable Material," report prepared for The National Commission on Materials Policy, August 1973, p. 5-4.
[13] See "National Parks Centennial," *E.R.R.*, 1972 Vol. I, pp. 125-144.
[14] Glen O. Robinson, *The Forest Service* (1975), p. 2.

tory...public lands wholly or in part covered with timber or undergrowth, whether of commercial value or not, as public reservations...." This bill "was enacted not merely without fanfare but without any evident realization by Congress of the far-reaching character of the power it conferred on the President to remove land from the public domain."[15]

Establishment of the National Forest System

In 1892, Congress saw fit to extend the Timber and Stone Act, and under its provisions much of the most destructive logging in the western states occurred. However, before President Harrison left office in 1893 he designated more than 13 million acres of national forest reserves, and President Cleveland added 4.5 million additional acres. But Cleveland refused to create any more reserves until Congress provided for the management and administration of these forests, and in 1896 a seven-member National Forest Commission was appointed. It recommended more reserves and a federal agency to oversee them and to regulate logging, mining and grazing. By promptly adding 13 reserves covering 21 million acres, Cleveland aroused a storm of protest among western timber and mineral interests.

Meanwhile, Congress was considering numerous bills to regulate and protect the forest reserves. After five years of debate it passed the Forest Management Act of 1897, usually called the Organic Act. The act states: "No national forest shall be established, except to improve and protect the forest within the boundaries, or for the purpose of securing favorable conditions of water flows, and to furnish a continuous supply of timber for the use and necessities of the citizens of the United States...."

One of the problems during these years was that the nation had very few trained foresters who knew how to manage the forests to ensure a permanent timber supply. Fortunately there was one man—Gifford Pinchot—who had been trained in Europe and practiced forestry on the Vanderbilt estate in North Carolina.

Pinchot became head of the division of forestry in the Department of Agriculture in 1898, and in 1905 succeeded in having the 85.6 million acres of national forest reserves transferred from the land office in the Department of the Interior to his division. Congress also changed the name of the agency to the Forest Service, and Pinchot used his influence with Theodore Roosevelt to see that more than 100 million acres of forest reserves were created during the Roosevelt administration. In 1907 the term "forest reserves" was changed to "national forests."

---

[15] *Ibid.*, p. 6.

In 1911, in the Weeks Act, Congress empowered the Forest Service to buy and restore land "necessary for the protection of navigable streams" and to undertake forest fire prevention programs on this land. Most of the land acquired under this law was in the eastern states. In 1924, Congress passed the Clark-McNary Act, permitting the government to buy land for timber production as well as watershed protection. It also authorized federal assistance to state and private forestry programs in the form of matching funds. The McSweeny-McNary Act of 1928 established an experimental forestry branch in the Forest Service to study scientific forest management, the Knutson-Vandenberg Act of 1930 required purchasers of national forest timber to help pay for reforestation, and the Fulmer Act of 1935 authorized federal aid to the states in acquisition of lands for state forests.[16]

Results of 1944 Change in Timber Tax Policy

Among the most significant pieces of legislation dealing with timber was a 1944 tax law that changed timber taxation policy. "Timber was eligible for the capital gains rate in those earlier years, but only when liquidated or disposed of in a lump-sum sale," stated a recent report of the Forest Industries Committee on Timber Valuation Taxation.[17] "Sustained yield timber management was not recognized for capital gains purposes. In other words, if you sold your timber gradually under a cutting agreement or cut it for processing in your own mill, your proceeds were taxed at ordinary income tax rates—generally twice the rate applying to other capital transactions."

Timber is now treated like other capital assets for tax purposes. The difference between the original cost and the sales price (or market value) of the standing timber is taxed at the long-term capital gain rate. Profits from log sales or lumber processing or marketing are taxed at the standard income rate. The 1944 tax law change apparently stimulated reforestation. Before that year the nation's timber supply was decreasing steadily. Annual tree planting in private forests rose from less than 100,000 acres per year in 1945 to more than 1.3 million acres in the 1960s. "Over 26 million acres of private lands have been planted, compared to only 3 million acres in all previous years," the report stated. "In 1970, six acres were planted in trees for every one acre in the period preceding World War II."

The development of tree farms also increased reforestation. The Weyerhaeuser Co. traces the first tree farm back to 1941, to a 130,000-acre tract in Grays Harbor County, Wash., which was partly owned by the company. By the mid-1940s there were 938

---

[16] For the legislative history, see *Congress and the Nation*, Vol. I (1965), pp. 1045-1060.
[17] "Timber—America's Renewable Resource," August 1975, p. 8.

tree farms covering 11 million acres. Today there are more than 31,000 tree farms with some 76 million acres in all 50 states.[18] Tree farming has enabled foresters to improve many of their techniques. Select seedlings are planted and tended for specified results when they are harvested as trees years later.

Response to Postwar Demands for More Lumber

The building boom after World War II created a tremendous demand for lumber. Timber prices shot up, and there was great pressure on the Forest Service to open up more national forest lands to logging. One response to the demand was increased road construction in the national forests—in 1940, there were only 87,000 miles of roads but by 1960 there were 160,000 miles. Timber sales also soared—the harvest from national forests rose from 1.5 billion board feet in 1941 to 4.4 billion in 1951 and 8.3 billion in 1961.[19] The increased emphasis on timber production led Congress to enact the Multiple Use-Sustained Yield Act of 1960. It declared as federal policy that the national forests should be managed for outdoor recreation, range, timber, watershed, and fish and wildlife resources. The act said that these various renewable surface resources should be "utilized in the combination that will best meet the needs of the American people."

Some have argued that the law's language is too vague to be administered, while others believe that the Forest Service has done an admirable job of multiple-use management. But it is clear that Congress has favored timber production over other uses through the appropriations process. From 1954 to 1970, the Forest Service received 66 per cent of its budget increase requests for timber sale administration, but only 20 per cent of the desired increases for recreation and wildlife, 17 per cent for reforestation and 15 per cent for soil and watershed management.[20]

Public concern over national forest management began to increase in the 1960s. A prime influence was the long fight for creation of a National Wilderness Preservation System, which culminated in the enactment of the Wilderness Act of 1964.[21] The purpose of the law was to set aside certain wild areas in the national forests for permanent protection from logging, mining, grazing, road-building and other commercial uses. Under the

[18] Statistics from an address by Charles W. Bingham, senior vice president for land and timber, Weyerhaeuser Co., to the American Forestry Association's sixth American Forest Congress, Washington, D.C., Oct. 7, 1975.

[19] "An Analysis of Forestry Issues in the First Session of the 92nd Congress," Congressional Research Service, Library of Congress, pp. 4-5.

[20] "Clearcutting on Federal Timberlands," report by the Subcommittee on Public Lands to the Committee on Interior and Insular Affairs, U.S. Senate, March 1972, pp. 6-7.

[21] See "Wilderness Preservation," *E.R.R.*, 1975 Vol. I, pp. 383-402.

1964 law and later supplementary legislation, 125 wilderness areas comprising 12.6 million acres have been set aside. About 400 other areas totaling almost 59 million acres are under study as potential additions.

Origins of the Controversy Over Clearcutting

A change in Forest Service practices during the early 1960s would eventually lead to a vitriolic national debate. In 1964, the service began the general application of clearcutting to eastern hardwood forests, which previously were harvested primarily by selection or shelterwood cutting methods *(see box, p. 121).* As public concern for ecology and the environment rose in the late 1960s and early 1970s, criticism of clearcutting began to grow. Since then, the Forest Service has said: "The first step was likely in the right direction but on the wrong foot. We did too much clearcutting, too soon, in concentrated areas..."[22]

The Forest Service was criticized especially for allowing large-scale clearcutting in four national forests—the Bitterroot and the Bridger in Wyoming, the Tongass in Alaska and the Monongahela in West Virginia. Indeed, the agency conducted several in-house studies which found that there had been lapses in multiple-use management and over-emphasis on timber production in these forests. And several independent investigations, including a report from a select committee from the University of Montana and a report by a special commission chosen by the West Virginia state legislature, confirmed that there had been serious abuses of clearcutting practices.[23]

In late 1971, the Council on Environmental Quality drew up guidelines on clearcutting and recommended that President Nixon issue an executive order limiting the practice on federal forest lands—prohibiting clearcutting in areas of scenic beauty, in places where soil erosion might result or where the forest might not regenerate promptly. But the order was never issued. A series of meetings at the White House with timber industry representatives led to its abandonment. That caused a widespread uproar against clearcutting and the introduction of several bills in Congress to ban or limit the practice.[24]

The Public Lands Subcommittee of the Senate Interior and Insular Affairs Committee held extensive hearings on clear-

---

[22] "Chronology of a Controversy—Monongahela's Timber," U.S. Forest Service report, September 1975, p. 2.

[23] "A University View of the Forest Service," prepared for the U.S. Senate Committee on Interior and Insular Affairs by a University of Montana committee led by Dean Arnold W. Bolle of the School of Forestry, Dec. 1, 1970; and "Report of the Forest Management Practices Commission," West Virginia legislature, August 1970. Another publication which aroused public opinion against clearcutting was Nancy Wood's *Clearcut—The Deforestation of America,* a 1971 Sierra Club "Battlebook."

[24] For background and details, see "Clearcutting: Pressures on Congress for Decision," *Congressional Quarterly Weekly Report,* March 4, 1972, pp. 492-496.

cutting in 1971 and issued a report the following March. It said clearcutting *should not* be practiced where soil, slope or other watershed conditions were fragile or subject to major damage; where there was no assurance that the area could be restocked within five years; where esthetic values were primary; or where the method was preferred only because it would give the greatest dollar return or unit output. The report said clearcutting *should* be employed where it was essential to accomplish forest management objectives; where the size of clearcuts was minimal; where the environmental, biological, esthetic, engineering and economic impact had been studied; and where clearcuts were shaped and blended into the natural terrain. The Forest Service has generally adopted these guidelines, which have come to be known as the Church guidelines in recognition of the Subcommittee Chairman, Sen. Frank Church (D Idaho).

Even so, clearcutting remains a source of controversy. "Clearcutting to the Sierra Club is like busing to George Wallace," said Robert E. Wolf, assistant chief of the environmental policy division of the Library of Congress' Congressional Research Service. "Being against busing really means you're against integration; being against clearcutting really means you're against all logging. It's a shorthand label for no timber cutting." But Tom Barlow of the NRDC said: "We're prepared to be reasonable on the clearcutting thing if the industry is prepared to meet us halfway." And Brock Evans of the Sierra Club said: "The Church guidelines were a start, but they're really vaguely worded, and can only be considered a starting point."

Pressures for Change in Forest Policy

IN ORDER to reconcile the conflicting demands being made upon the nation's forests and to resolve the controversy over forest management practices, some observers believe that an official national policy should be established. This would be even broader than the "comprehensive" bills being proposed to Congress. These apply only to the national forests whereas the envisioned policy would cover all of the nation's forest lands. The directors of the American Forestry Association, at their centennial meeting in October 1975, called upon Congress to take immediate steps to "avert a forestry crunch" by establishing such a policy.

The President's Advisory Panel on Timber and the Environment, in its April 1973 report, made 20 major recommendations on forest policy. They included: a national program of

Timber Harvesting Methods

Even-aged Management. Trees in a given stand are maintained at about the same age and size, and harvested at once so that a new stand may grow. The three basic even-aged methods are:

Clearcutting. The removal of an entire stand of trees in blocks, patches or strips, followed by natural regeneration, artificial seeding or hand planting of seedlings.

Shelterwood. The removal of marketable trees in a series of cuts to allow regeneration of a new stand under the partial shade cover of older trees, which are later removed.

Seed Tree. The removal of nearly all marketable trees in one cut, except a small number of desirable seed bearers to provide for natural regeneration.

Uneven-aged Management. Trees in a given stand are maintained at all ages and all sizes to permit continuous natural regeneration. The primary even-aged method is:

Selection. The removal of marketable trees singly or in small groups at periodic intervals to produce a stand with different ages and sizes intermingled.

forest development and timber supply; completion of the National Wilderness Preservation System; restrictions on timber cutting on lands that cannot be logged without unacceptable environmental damage; new standards for road building and logging practices; periodic reviews of timber supply and demand; increases of 50 to 100 per cent in the annual harvest of commercial old growth timber in western national forests; accelerated programs of timber growing and regeneration on the national forests; incentive programs to encourage private landowners to manage their forests and increase timber supply; an increase in technological research on forest management and wood utilization; better financing of forest management programs; and creation of a permanent national forest policy board.

There have been a number of other reports in recent years dealing with timber supply and forest policy questions. "Material Needs and the Environment Today and Tomorrow," the final report of the National Commission on Materials Policy, was issued in June 1973 and a supplementary report, "Timber: The Renewable Material," by former U.S. Forest Service Chief Edward P. Cliff, was released in August 1973. Both reports recommended comprehensive reviews of American forest policies and new legislative and administrative action. In 1974, *The Last Stand,* Ralph Nader's study group report on the national forests, was published containing 28 major recommendations on national forest policy. In June 1974, Resources for the Future, Inc., a non-profit research and educational organization in Washington, D.C., published the proceedings of a forum on "Forest Policy for the Future: Conflict, Compromise, Consensus" in which environmentalists, foresters and timber industry representatives all participated. Marion Clawson, acting president of Resources for the Future, later produced a book entitled *Forests For Whom and For What?* (1975) in which he set forth various forest policy issues and alternatives and offered a framework for forest policy analysis.

Indeed, there have been so many studies, reports and recommendations in the past few years that Sen. Mark O. Hatfield (R Ore.) remarked at the recent American Forestry Association meeting: "While problems have surfaced periodically relating to timber supply, wilderness or recreation, the reaction has been consistently insufficient and can be summarized in two words: study it." There have been proposals in all of these reports on which those on all sides of the issue could agree—such as the need for long-range, well-funded forestry programs, increased emphasis on small private forests, and more attention to the 75 million acres needing reforestation. An urgent need, most agree, is for expanded and consistent federal funding.

Funds for forest management and reforestation programs come from two basic sources—general funds under the 1897 Organic Act and funds for logged areas that private industry must pay under the Knutson-Vandenberg Act of 1930. The objective of the 1930 act was to require contract purchasers of federal timber to plant or seed lands they cut, with funds set aside at the time of purchase. But these funds must be used in the area logged, and they may not exceed the average cost of planting comparable national forest lands during the previous three years. Many foresters complain this is not adequate for complete reforestation. Moreover, the Office of Management and Budget for the past several years has regularly reduced or impounded funds budgeted for the Forest Service, blaming the federal deficit.

Potential of Improving Utilization of Timber

Of all the recommendations, the most dramatic results probably could be produced by better utilization of wood and protection of the forests from fire and pest damage. About one-fifth of the annual timber growth is lost to fire, insects and disease. This amounts to about $500 million worth of timber, equal to about 30 per cent of the annual harvest. In the national forests of the Northwest—where most of the nation's prime housing and construction timber grows—the loss amounts to about half of the current allowable harvest throughout the national forest system.

Improved utilization includes better use of logging and milling residues such as bark, limbs, and sawdust; improved wood processing and development of new forms of plywood and pulpwood; prolonging the life of wood products through special treatment; more recycling of paper products; and improved timber harvesting methods such as balloon, helicopter and skyline cable logging.

Firewood has been a fuel for much of the world's population for centuries,[25] but new technologies have made it possible to use wood wastes efficiently as fuel in electric power plants. A special task force in Vermont earlier this year found that the number of "culls"—trees unsuitable for use as saw logs or veneer—produced in the state's forests every year was sufficient to supply Vermont's annual electrical requirements.

Calls for Multiple Use Management of Forests

Controversy over American forest policies will continue until a way is found to balance the often conflicting demands of various interest groups while ensuring an adequate timber supply to meet public needs. That ideal resolution of differences may be impossible to achieve. "You've got the extreme groups who want to lock it all up in wilderness on the one hand and on the other hand you've got the extreme groups who want to exploit it all for timber," said Larry Jahn of the Wildlife Management Institute. "When you blend the two, you get rational management." But Jahn is not entirely sanguine about the chances for such a compromise. "The terms 'multiple use' and 'sustained yield' are like a Holy Grail, but they're a long way from being a reality. We're still in the phase of bringing about a balance. We're still in the middle of implementing the 1960 act."

The vague language of the 1960 act has given rise to many conflicts over its application. A basic question concerns whether multiple use is possible for all parts of all forests at all times, or whether some forests must be managed for primary uses and secondary uses. "It's easy to manage forests—or any land, for that matter—to maximize the output of timber, or grazing, or recreation, or fish and wildlife, or for any other single purpose," Lynn A. Greenwalt, director of the U.S. Fish and Wildlife Service, told the American Forestry Association at its 1975 meeting. "It's not so easy to manage lands to provide a mixture, an array, of benefits." But there is growing recognition that the future of the nation's forests depends on their ability to provide that array of benefits to the satisfaction of all the beneficiaries.

---

[25] There is a severe firewood shortage in many parts of the world as a result of petroleum price increases. See "The Other Energy Crisis: Firewood," by Erik P. Eckholm, Worldwatch Paper No. 1, Worldwatch Institute, September 1975.

Selected Bibliography

Books

Barney, Daniel R., *The Last Stand—Ralph Nader's Study Group Report on the National Forests*, Grossman Publishers, 1974.
Clawson, Marion, *Forests For Whom and For What?* Resources for the Future, Inc., The Johns Hopkins University Press, 1975.
Horwitz, Eleanor C. J., *Clearcutting: A View From the Top*, Acropolis Books Ltd., 1974.
Robinson, Glen O., *The Forest Service: A Study in Public Land Management*, Resources for the Future, Inc., The Johns Hopkins University Press, 1975.
Wood, Nancy, *Clearcut: The Deforestation of America*, Sierra Club, 1971.

Articles

Journal of Forestry, selected issues.
Sierra Club Bulletin, selected issues.

Studies and Reports

American Enterprise Institute for Public Policy Research, "Forest Management and Timber Supply Legislation," Legislative Analysis No. 17, May 6, 1974.
American Forest Institute, "Forests USA," July 1974.
Clawson, Marion (ed.), "Forest Policy for the Future," Resources for the Future, Inc., June 1974.
Forest Industries Committee on Timber Valuation Taxation, "Timber —America's Renewable Resource," August 1975.
Forest Industries Management Center, University of Oregon, "Ecology, Environmentalism, and Future Timber Supply," March 18, 1975.
Cliff, Edward P., "Timber: The Renewable Material," National Commission on Materials Policy, August 1973.
"Report of the President's Advisory Panel on Timber and the Environment," April 1973.
U.S. Department of Agriculture, Forest Service, "Chronology of a Controversy—Monongahela's Timber," September 1975.
—"Environmental Program for the Future," draft, August 1974.
—"RPA"—Summary, Program and Assessment for the Nation's Renewable Resources (3 volumes), as required by the Forest and Rangeland Renewable Resources Planning Act of 1974, August 1975.
—"The Outlook for Timber in the United States," Forest Resource Report No. 20, July 1974.
U.S. Office of Education, Land Use Letter No. 1, "Our National Forests: Can They Meet Future Needs?" April 1975.
U.S. Senate Committee on Interior and Insular Affairs, "A University View of the Forest Service," Select Committee of the University of Montana, Dec. 1, 1970.
—Subcommittee on Public Lands, "Clearcutting on Federal Timberlands," March 1972.

WESTERN WATER: COMING CRISIS

by

Tom Arrandale

Jan. 14
1 9 7 7

WESTERN WATER: COMING CRISIS

WATER ALWAYS has been precious in the American West. Early 19th-century mapmakers described most of the region as the "Great American Desert." The scarcity of water in this brown and empty landscape has confined human occupation since the earliest Indian and Spanish settlements. Later settlers dammed the rivers and pierced the underground reservoirs, but the most they created were scattered oases of farms and towns across the high plains and dry uplands.

"The overriding influence that shapes the West is the desert," University of Texas historian Walter Prescott Webb maintained. "That is its one unifying force."[1] Twentieth-century engineering has enlisted the Colorado River and other western rivers in the fight to subdue the desert. But the desert endures, and now threatens to cut short western economic progress.

Already agricultural irrigation is exhausting groundwater resources stored up over thousands of years. Many western cities are rapidly outgrowing sustainable water supplies. The once-mighty Colorado River, the lifeline for half of the western population, could be fully committed to human consumption by 1990 or earlier. Entire states and regions are skirmishing over limited river flows, with the economic prospects brought by assured water supplies at stake.

Water use already has passed renewable natural supply in some western areas, and demand for water is accelerating. The national shift of population and economic power to the Southwest "Sunbelt" and Rocky Mountain states can only reinforce the trend. The expected national drive to develop the West's vast energy resources adds yet another potential claim upon dwindling water reserves. American Indian tribes are laying claim to ancestral water rights, while environmentalists are fighting to preserve many rivers, streams and lakes in a natural state.

Without massive efforts to enlarge supplies—by diverting faraway rivers or by augmenting natural precipitation—or to conserve supplies, the West will face more bitter struggles over water. Expanding cities and booming industries, wielding great

---

[1] "The American West—Perpetual Mirage," *Harper's*, May 1957, p. 25.

economic power, already have begun taking over water rights from irrigated farms. The shift of water away from agriculture, as suburban developments and industrial parks spread onto neighboring fields, threatens the region with painful political, social and economic adjustments.

"We've been so concerned with the idea that we must get our share," Sierra Club President Brant Calkin said in an interview, that western dam-building and well-drilling "have gone beyond the point of diminishing return." A study by Resources for the Future, a Washington, D.C., research organization, found that sections of the West with the smallest natural water endowments have begun using water in a "highly water-consumptive" fashion.[2]

Nationwide Concern Over Water Supplies

Western water problems are merely the cutting edge of a disturbing long-range trend in national water supply and demand. "A natural resource more precious than oil is in increasingly short supply in many parts of America," *U.S. News & World Report* said recently. "Water, if present trends continue, seems likely to provoke the next crisis with nationwide impact."[3] The nation's water concerns were amplified by drought conditions that threatened crop production from the Midwest to California during 1976. And a study by the U.S. Army Corps of Engineers warned that the highly populated northeastern states—particularly the Boston, New York and Washington, D.C., metropolitan areas—were growing more vulnerable to droughts that could bring drinking-water shortages.[4]

Leo F. Laporte of the University of California at Santa Cruz, in a recent study of national water prospects, concluded: "For most of the country, water demand in the year 2000 will significantly exceed supply. Of the major drainage basins within the 48 states only three—regions in the Northeast, Southeast and Ohio Valley—will have an assured supply of water in the year 2000 if current trends of water use and consumption continue. In other regions—Mid-Atlantic, Midwest and Northwest—supply will be greater than consumption, but in-channel water [that used in streams and returned] will be in short supply unless we change certain laws and encourage multiple use of water. In the remainder—mostly the West—projected future demand grossly exceeds the total supply."[5]

Most Americans always have taken ample water for granted. But dwindling water supplies may create situations comparable

[2] Charles W. Howe and K. William Easter, *Interbasin Transfers of Water* (1971), p. 3.

[3] "Coast to Coast—Water Becomes a Big Worry," *U.S. News & World Report*, Sept. 6, 1976, p. 27.

[4] See "World Weather Trends," *E.R.R.*, 1974 Vol. II, pp. 517-538.

[5] Leo F. Laporte, *Encounter With the Earth: Resources* (1975), p. 83.

Human Use of Water

In contrast to minerals and fossil fuels, water is a renewable resource, constantly circulating through the earth's hydrosphere in a cycle of precipitation, evaporation and surface flow. Only about 30 per cent of the vast amount of water in annual circulation falls on the land, and only about 10 per cent of that becomes available for human use.

In the United States, about 4.4 trillion gallons of water fall on the land surface each day. About 70 per cent of the rainfall and snowfall returns to the air through surface evaporation or plant transpiration—the process whereby vegetation draws water up through root systems and evaporates it from leaf surfaces. The remaining 30 per cent of annual U.S. precipitation—some 1.1 trillion gallons a day—runs off the land into rivers, streams, lakes, ponds or subsurface groundwater deposits.

In the past 20 years, industry has surpassed agriculture as the largest U.S. water user, taking some 58 per cent of the water diverted in 1970. Irrigation withdrew about 35 per cent, public water utilities 7 per cent and rural domestic uses 1 per cent. Even so, industry returned most of its water to the streamflow, although pollution made large amounts unfit for other uses. Irrigation was by far the nation's largest water consumer, accounting for nearly 90 per cent of total consumptive uses—mostly in the West.

Total U.S. water withdrawals have multiplied nine times since 1900, to 370 billion gallons a day from 40 billion gallons a day. Individual consumption has soared to an average of 160 gallons per person a day, compared to about 10 gallons per person daily around the turn of the century.

to wartime commodity shortages or the 1973-74 oil crisis. Several observers have predicted a strong reaction among Americans confronting scarce water supplies and possible government regulation of water use.

Critical Situation That Confronts the West

The potential crunch between supply and demand clearly is most ominous in the West, where treeless prairies, bare mountains, dry lakes and trickling rivers offer centuries-old testimony to the meager flow of water. While rich in minerals, scenery and land, most of the West is water-poor. From the 100th meridian, which runs through the heart of the Great Plains, westward nearly to the Pacific Ocean the West is dry and sometimes parched. The only sizable exceptions are a narrow coastal strip from Washington through northern California and the high elevations of the Sierra Nevada and Rocky Mountains.

Rainfall declines progressively westward from the 100th meridian, averaging 20 inches a year or less, while combined evaporation and plant transpiration rates are high. The mountain ranges are partly responsible for the interior aridity. As warm and wet air from over the Pacific Ocean climbs their western slopes the water vapor cools and falls as rain, generally leaving little for the eastern side. The dry air masses then pick up more moisture from the land as they move down the other side of the mountains.

As a result, most streams west of the 100th meridian flow only part of the year, usually during brief rainy seasons or during the spring "runoff" of melting snow in the mountains. Summer thunderstorms often result in flash floods, since sun-baked streambeds and arroyos are unable to handle the sudden downpours—a curse of plenty in a water-deprived land. The West's few year-round streams—including the Rio Grande, the Colorado, the Pacific coastal rivers, the Snake-Columbia system, the Missouri and its tributaries—rise in the mountain areas and take much of their flow from melting snowpacks.

Despite the prevailing dry climate, the earth over thousands of years has stored substantial amounts of groundwater beneath the arid western landscape. In many areas, the flow of water through underground aquifers—the water-bearing rock strata such as sandstone and limestone—is interconnected with the flow of rivers and streams on the surface. A U.S. Interior Department study in 1975 estimated that 6.2 billion acre-feet of water are stored beneath the 11 westernmost states at depths from 50 to 200 feet.[6]

But in many western regions, groundwater is being depleted much faster than natural processes can recharge it. Surface waters, particularly in the critical Colorado River system, most likely cannot supply the growing demands of population shifts and energy projects. Irrigation with groundwater has been "mining" the aquifers, withdrawing water at rates far in excess of the slow recharging process. The increased reliance on groundwater was made possible by technological improvements since World War II in drilling techniques and pumping efficiency from deep wells, and by relatively inexpensive energy from electricity and natural gas. On the High Plains stretching from the 100th meridian to the Rocky Mountains, agricultural irrigation has expanded enormously in the past three decades as farmers tapped the Ogallala Formation, a huge underground aquifer that extends southward from the Platte River under western Nebraska, Kansas, Oklahoma and Texas into eastern Colorado and New Mexico.

---

[6] Bureau of Reclamation, Department of the Interior, *Critical Water Problems Facing the Eleven Western States,* executive summary, April 1975, p. 4. An acre-foot is the volume of water needed to cover one acre of land to a depth of one foot; equal to 43,560 cubic feet or 325,851 gallons. The 11 states are Arizona, California, Colorado, Idaho, Montana, New Mexico, Nevada, Oregon, Utah, Washington and Wyoming.

Today, however, groundwater tables are falling precipitously. In some areas overlying the Ogallala Formation, the low output from wells and their higher drilling costs are making irrigation prohibitively expensive. Some Texas and New Mexico farmers have been forced to resort to "dry land farming," which depends solely on sporadic rainfall. The 1975 Interior Department study predicted that irrigation activity in eastern New Mexico "will begin to decline significantly by about 1980." And in 1973 the National Water Commission issued a massive study of U.S. water prospects, forecasting "precipitous declines in agricultural production" in western Texas by 1990. It predicted that irrigated agricultural tracts in that area by the year 2015 would decline to 125,000 acres from 4 million acres, and the value of agricultural production to $128-million annually from $430-million.[7] Other western states, including California, the nation's biggest producer of farm goods, also are affected.

Natural and Human-Caused Complications

The usefulness of the West's limited supplies of surface water and groundwater has been reduced, moreover, by natural and human-caused problems. Increasing salinity in the lower reaches of southwestern rivers and in vast groundwater stores is a serious constraint. While relatively free from industrial and municipal pollution, many western streams carry high concentrations of minerals absorbed from the rock formations they pass through. Irrigation and other human uses have increased these natural concentrations by leaving less water to dilute the salt loads. Sometimes crop yields are cut and fields forced out of production by the high salt content in the water.

Salinity levels in the Colorado River have prompted complaints from the Mexican government that U.S. withdrawals were reducing the quality of Mexico's allocation of river water granted under a 1944 treaty. In 1973, President Nixon and Mexican President Luis Echeverria signed an agreement committing the United States to limit salinity in water flowing into Mexico. Congress in 1974 authorized construction of a large desalinization plant and other measures to help meet that commitment.[8]

Another problem is the proliferation of water-consuming vegetation along rivers and irrigation ditches. Such long-rooted plants, known as phreatophytes, include willow, cottonwood, ash and walnut trees. About 16 million acres of land in the Southwest are covered by such vegetation. Along the Gila River in southern Arizona, for example, phreatophytes that cover 11,-

---

[7] *Water Policies for the Future—Final Report to the President and to the Congress of the United States,* June 1973, p. 239. The commission was created in 1968 to study national water resource problems and to issue a comprehensive report.

[8] See *Congressional Quarterly 1974 Almanac,* pp. 827-829.

200 acres consume about 40,000 acre-feet of water a year, according to the National Water Commission. But phreatophytes also offer important wildlife habitat. Saltcedar, one widespread species, is commonly found in the Bosque del Apache National Wildlife Refuge along the Rio Grande in New Mexico, which has become a vital wintering ground for some of the few whooping cranes in existence. Phreatophytes also reduce evaporation by protecting stream surfaces from the sun and wind.

The numerous large lakes and reservoirs built throughout the West to store surface water for use during dry cycles increase water evaporation by exposing larger surfaces to the air. Evaporation losses from 124,000-acre Lake Mead, formed by the Colorado River behind Hoover Dam, have been estimated at 849,000 acre-feet a year. And Lake Powell, created along the Colorado by Glen Canyon Dam, is losing substantial amounts of water through seepage into porous sandstone in the canyon walls, according to hydrologists.

Heavy Demands of the Booming 'Sunbelt'

Water supply problems are expected to become more critical as the nation's population and economic power shifts southward and westward. The highly publicized Sunbelt, the southern rim of states where development has been outpacing the rest of the country, includes rapidly growing metropolitan centers in some of the driest parts of the Southwest. Since World War II the western states have boomed. New industries and government installations have sprung up, and professional and retired people have flocked in, attracted by hospitable climates, scenic beauties and growth-oriented policies. In the last three decades, population has increased by 197 per cent in Nevada, 91 per cent in Colorado, 75 per cent in Utah and 68 per cent in New Mexico. And in contrast to other regions, where people have been moving away from troubled central cities, the western influx has concentrated in spreading urban centers.[9]

That kind of growth brings with it new demands for water, not only for drinking and other basic needs, but also for recreation, car washing and lawn sprinkling. It also leads to water commitments that are difficult if not impossible to reduce once they are made. Calkin of the Sierra Club commented: "Once people are involved, the commitment remains as long as the people are there." Western state economies are expected to continue diversifying, as well. The growing importance of defense, electronic and service industries has left these states less dependent on farming and mining, the economic bases in the first half of this century. In Arizona, for instance, agricultural and mining in-

---

[9]See "The Shift to Sunbelt: What It Means for Cities," *National Urban Coalition Network,* summer 1976, pp. 1-3.

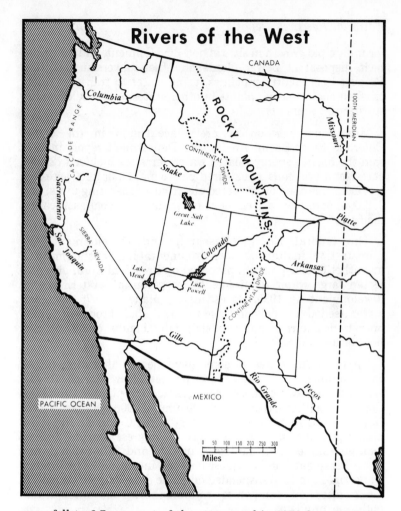

Rivers of the West

come fell to 6.7 per cent of the state total in 1970 from 21.5 per cent in 1940.[10] Although agriculture continued to withdraw and consume the largest volume of water, growing cities and developing industries began competing fiercely for the state's severely limited supplies. This is the problem that confronts most of the states in the American West today.

Needs of Potential Energy Development

Western water problems could become more acute if the region's vast energy resources are developed more fully. The West contains 70 per cent of the nation's strippable coal reserves, vast oil-bearing shale deposits, major uranium reserves and important geothermal energy sources. If the nation claims these resources, water will be needed for mining and processing,

---

[10] Maurice M. Kelso, William E. Martin and Lawrence E. Mack, *Water Supplies and Economic Growth in an Arid Environment* (1973), pp. 12-16.

for municipal growth in sites of new development, and for waste-heat disposal at power plants and fuel-conversion facilities. Proposed coal slurry pipelines, using water to transport finely crushed coal to power plants in other states, also would require substantial amounts.

Many energy resources are concentrated in the Upper Colorado River Basin. An Interior Department report in 1974 said the basin's energy-related water demands included 125,000 acre-feet a year for six coal-fired power plants, 351,000 acre-feet a year for planned or projected electricity-generating units, and 388,000 acre-feet a year for oil-shale and coal-gasification facilities.[11]

The federal Energy Research and Development Administration, in drafting an environmental impact statement on a synthetic fuels program proposed by President Ford, also projected large water requirements for potential western energy development by 1985. Its estimates, made in 1975, included water needed for coal conversion and oil-shale processing, mine operations and reclamation of strip-mined lands, and associated population increases.[12]

Upper Basin states already have begun allocating future water supplies to proposed energy projects. New Mexico officials estimate that two proposed coal-gasification plants in the Four Corners area[13] together would consume 63,000 acre-feet a year from the San Juan River, a tributary of the Colorado. But these plants probably will be built only if Congress provides federal loan guarantees, and the House in 1975 and 1976 twice turned down President Ford's request for such incentives. The Interior Department in 1976 suspended oil-shale development on federal lands after oil companies running tests encountered air-pollution problems.[14]

Indian Claims and Environmental Issues

Another potential water demand that could disrupt all western water-resource planning is the issue of water rights of American Indians. In the past, water development projects largely ignored the Indians' rights to water in streams flowing through their reservations. In recent years, however, various tribes have made substantial water claims that are based on Supreme Court decisions giving them priority over other water users.

---

[11] Department of the Interior, "Report on Water for Energy in the Upper Colorado River Basin," 1974, p. 40.

[12] Energy Research and Development Administration, "Synthetic Fuels Commercialization Program, Draft Environmental Impact Statement," December 1975, pp. VII-9 to VII-16.

[13] Where the boundaries of Arizona, Colorado, New Mexico and Utah join.

[14] For background, see "Oil Shale Development," *E.R.R.*, 1968 Vol. II, pp. 905-922.

The court laid the foundation for Indian water rights in 1908, in ruling against water diversions upstream from the Fort Belknap Reservation on the Milk River in Montana. The court declared that creation of the reservation implicitly gave the Indians a right to use its waters. So the doctrine of prior appropriation, giving preferred rights to the first person to divert a stream for use, was ruled inapplicable on Indian reservations.[15] In a 1963 decision allocating Lower Colorado Basin water, the court affirmed the 1908 doctrine and went on to set a standard for water rights on reservations used primarily for farming. In assigning nearly one million acre-feet of Colorado River water to five Indian reservations, the court accepted an allocation based on the amount of Indian land that could be irrigated practically.[16] The water rights of other Indian reservations still are being disputed in the courts.

Growing national concern for environmental values adds another potential claim on water supplies. In the past, laws based on the appropriation doctrine made little provision for non-economic values. But several western states now have enacted legislation recognizing the continued flow of water as beneficial for recreation, scenery and fish and wildlife. Several federal environmental laws also are aimed at keeping western waters in their natural state. Such demands will create stiff competition for water with irrigated agriculture, cities and industries. "There are going to be some very crucial direct confrontations between agriculture, municipalities and energy industries, and there's going to be fierce competition between the states," Harris Sherman, director of the Colorado Department of Natural Resources, has predicted.[17]

Oasis Development of the West

THE WEST's predominant dryness inevitably shaped and limited human efforts to establish lasting settlements. The late Walter Prescott Webb, with his historical insight, called the West "virtually an oasis civilization," with cities and farms clustered about natural and artificial water supplies. Native American farming cultures tended to locate along rivers and streams, and even ancient cliff-dwelling villages depended on floodwater to farm the valley bottoms. The Hohokam Indians established extensive irrigation systems in central Arizona, and

---

[15] *Winters v. U.S.*, 207 U.S. 564 (1908).
[16] *Arizona v. California*, 373 U.S. 546 (1963).
[17] Quoted by Grace Lichtenstein in *The New York Times*, Aug. 22, 1976.

16th-century Spanish explorers found a string of Pueblo villages along fields irrigated by the Rio Grande. In more than 200 years of occupation, the Spaniards never settled much beyond the Rio Grande Valley.

The West's dry regions remained a barrier to expansion from Atlantic Coast states well into the 19th century. The scarcity of water and other crucial materials such as wood made prospects unappealing west of the Mississippi River Valley. Historian Daniel J. Boorstin noted that popular conceptions of the Great Plains as a "waterless, treeless, uninhabitable desert" delayed settlement for decades in a region that later became part of the nation's breadbasket.[18]

After traveling across the plains to the Rocky Mountains in 1819-20, Stephen H. Long of the U.S. Topographical Engineers reported the region "almost wholly unfit for cultivation, and of course uninhabitable by a people depending upon agriculture for their subsistence."[19] Long's 1823 map labeled the area the "Great American Desert." But settlers still pushed across the prairies, notably up the Platte River and other Missouri tributaries. Transcontinental railroads, built after the Civil War to link the Pacific Coast with the Mississippi Valley, encouraged the "sodbusters." But farming in the West was tenuous, even during wet cycles, and vulnerable to the devastating droughts that seemed to come roughly every 20 years. The 11 western states nonetheless grew in population during the last half of the 19th century nearly 10 times faster than the country as a whole.[20]

Legacy of the Reclamation Act of 1902

But the all-out effort to conquer the desert came after the turn of the century, as new technology was used to rechannel available water resources to areas of need. The federal government, under the Reclamation Act of 1902, began promoting western economic development through massive irrigation, hydroelectric and flood-control projects on the Colorado, Columbia and other rivers. The law provided for particular assistance to homestead-sized farms. It directed the Bureau of Reclamation to require recipients of irrigation water from its projects to repay the federal government in 10 years, but only for capital construction costs and without interest charges. The 10-year repayment period later was extended in stages, eventually to 50 years or more. As the law was interpreted, moreover, even the interest-free capital charges were repaid only according to ability to pay. But even with such favorable terms,

---

[18] Daniel J. Boorstin, *The Americans: The National Experience* (1965), p. 223.

[19] Quoted by Boorstin, p. 229.

[20] See "Rural Migration," *E.R.R.*, 1975 Vol. II, p. 590.

Colorado River System

- Flaming Gorge Dam
- WYO.
- COLO.
- Green River
- Gunnison
- UTAH
- NEV.
- RIVER BASIN BOUNDARY
- Colorado River
- San Juan
- Glen Canyon Dam
- UPPER BASIN
- DRAINAGE BASIN BOUNDARY
- Las Vegas
- Hoover Dam
- Grand Canyon
- LOWER BASIN
- NEW MEXICO
- Davis Dam
- Little Colorado
- Central Arizona Unit Aqueduct System
- Los Angeles
- CALIF.
- Colorado River
- Parker Dam
- Phoenix
- ARIZONA
- Salt
- Gila River
- PACIFIC OCEAN
- MEXICO

the repayment records of most federal reclamation projects have been poor. Studies have estimated the total federal subsidy at more than 90 per cent on several major projects, including many of those in the Colorado River basin *(above)*.

By 1969, according to National Water Commission figures, Bureau of Reclamation projects had irrigated 8.6 million acres. That was roughly one-fifth of the nation's total irrigated land of 39.1 million acres, which included 34.8 million acres in 17 western states.[21] A study sponsored by consumer advocate Ralph Nader summarized the resulting accomplishments: "Since 1902 $6-billion have been poured into reclamation projects in the 17 westernmost states and Hawaii....Bureau water has converted what was once arid wasteland into fertile fields; Bureau hydroelectric power has contributed to the growth of western cities; and Bureau dams have helped prevent many potential floods and created vast lakes for recreation."[22]

---

[21] *Water Policies for the Future*, pp. 126-128. The states are the 11 listed in footnote 6 plus the Dakotas, Kansas, Nebraska, Oklahoma and Texas.

[22] Richard L. Berkman and W. Kip Viscusi, *Damming the West* (1973), pp. 1-4.

Nonetheless, the Nader study, the National Water Commission and other water experts have been highly critical of the Bureau of Reclamation. They have challenged the economic efficiency of large federal subsidies to irrigate naturally dry regions. While irrigation, flood-control and power projects have brought undeniable benefits to local and regional economies in the West, taxpayers throughout the nation have borne the costs. In addition, critics contend, the costs have included the loss of jobs and income in regions not served by reclamation projects, and—until the world food demand reached present levels—the production of large agricultural surpluses requiring federal subsidies in the form of price supports.

Urban Use of Aqueducts and Groundwater

Federal water diversion projects, along with similar developments by state and municipal governments, also have made possible the growth of many western cities into major metropolitan areas. Los Angeles and Denver both are dependent on large scale water-transfer projects. After exhausting its local supply, Los Angeles reached out for water from California's mountainous regions. The 233-mile-long Los Angeles Aqueduct was completed in 1913 to bring water from Owens Valley on the eastern slopes of the Sierra Nevada.

Denver, at the eastern edge of the Rocky Mountains, takes more than half of its water from Colorado's "western slope," on the Pacific side of the Continental Divide. Denver began diverting water in 1936 from tributaries of the Colorado River. Subsequent projects, some built primarily to supplement irrigation supplies on the eastern Colorado plains, pump water to the Denver region in tunnels cut through the mountains.[23]

Other burgeoning western cities have relied mainly on tapping groundwater to meet their needs. In New Mexico, groundwater supplies roughly half of the total water depleted each year. Public water supply systems, including that of the Albuquerque area where more than one-third of the state's population is concentrated, draw 94 per cent of their water from underground. Arizona pumps 60 per cent of its annual water withdrawals from groundwater reservoirs, and the city of Tucson is entirely dependent on groundwater.

The oasis development discerned by historian Webb has resulted in a paradoxical demographic pattern: amid fabled wide-open spaces, the western population increasingly has concentrated in urban areas replete with shopping centers, car washes and manicured lawns. Author Georg Borgstrom contends that westerners thus lost touch with the fundamental

---

[23] For a brief review of water transfer projects, see Howe and Easter, pp. 6-9.

Chronology of the Colorado

The Colorado River drains a 243,000-square-mile area, including some of the nation's driest—but fastest-growing—states. The river supplies about 17 million people in places as far apart as Los Angeles, Denver, Phoenix, Albuquerque and Salt Lake City. The Colorado and its tributaries have been diverted for human use since the 1850s, but the all-out effort to control the river began in the 1920s. Key steps in harnessing the Colorado included:

1922. The Colorado River Compact divided the interstate system into two areas—the Upper Basin (Wyoming, Colorado, Utah, New Mexico) and the Lower Basin (Arizona, California, Nevada). Each area was given perpetual rights to use an average of 7.5 million acre-feet each year.

1928. Congress passed the Boulder Canyon Act authorizing construction of the Hoover Dam and power plant, completed in 1936. The act also allocated the Lower Basin's water among California (4.4 million acre-feet), Arizona (2.8 million acre-feet) and Nevada (300,000 acre-feet).

1944. The Mexican Water Treaty committed the United States to deliver at least 1.5 million acre-feet of Colorado River flow to Mexico annually, except in times of extreme shortage.

1948. The Upper Colorado River Basin Compact devised a formula for sharing the river flow in excess of the annual average of 7.5 million acre-feet, giving Colorado 51.75 per cent, Utah 23 per cent, Wyoming 14 per cent and New Mexico 11.25 per cent.

1956. The Colorado River Storage Act authorized major reclamation projects in the Upper Basin and provided for construction of four major dams, including Glen Canyon Dam, completed in 1964.

1963. The Supreme Court, in *Arizona v. California,* ruled that the 1928 allocations were binding and that Arizona was entitled to full use of the Gila River before it reached the Colorado.

1968. The Colorado River Basin Project Act authorized construction of the Central Arizona Project to use Arizona's 2.8 million acre-foot entitlement, guaranteed California at least 4.4 million acre-feet even in times of shortage, and placed a 10-year moratorium on studies of interbasin transfers from other river systems, particularly the Columbia and Snake.

reality of living in a desert region. "It is almost forgotten," Borgstrom wrote, "that the 19th-century West of North America was won largely through a harsh adjustment to the strongly felt limitations of locally available water. There is a shrill contrast between these prime settlers and the excessively wasteful dwellers of our days."[24]

---

[24] Georg Borgstrom, *Too Many: An Ecological Overview of the Earth's Limitations* (1969), p. 169.

Coping With Water Shortages

WESTERN STATES are approaching a fundamental choice between living with their water constraints and trying to augment the natural water supply. Water management programs can help, but they will only delay inevitable shortages. "The changes in our social and economic structure are going to be enormous," cautions Calkins of the Sierra Club, predicting that "all the ills that have gone with unplanned growth in the past will be repeated." Proposals to augment the natural water resources in the West face formidable economic and environmental obstacles. The feasibility of water augmentation plans—through large-scale transfers from distant river basins, weather modification or desalinization—will depend on technological advances or on widespread water shortages that will make the costs involved seem acceptable.

Inter-basin transfers—projects that would apply current water diversion practices on a massive scale—have been on engineers' drawing boards for years. A study in 1971 by Resources for the Future listed 19 regional water transfer proposals, most of them variations of plans for supplying the Southwest with water diverted from the Columbia, the Mississippi or even Alaskan and Canadian rivers. The construction costs ranged up to $100-billion for a grandiose plan to supply water to 33 states, seven Canadian provinces and three states in northern Mexico.[25]

Economists generally have concluded that such massive inter-basin transfers "are just too costly," R. G. Cummings, a University of New Mexico professor of resource economics, said in an interview. The Columbia Basin transfer ideas, for instance, originated "in the days of cheap energy." He added: "You're talking about moving water uphill." Political obstacles may be even more formidable. Acceptance of the Central Arizona Project *(see opposite page)* was partly contingent on a 10-year moratorium on the study of inter-basin transfers from the Columbia River system. The moratorium is due to expire in 1978, but Northwest congressional delegations are expected to push for an extension to protect Columbia waters for development in their own states.

Pressures for inter-basin projects could increase, however, as areas of the West approach the limits of existing supplies. In 1976, for instance, Congress approved a $6-million federal study of possible ways to increase water supplies in High Plains areas dependent on dwindling Ogallala Formation groundwater. "The

[25] Howe and Easter, *op. cit.,* pp. 4-7, 168-175.

day is here, and the problem is going to get larger as time goes along," said Carl Slingerland of the New Mexico Interstate Stream Commission. Eventually, he added, "you have to decide whether you're going to move water to people or people to the water."

Weather Modification and Desalinization

Weather modification and desalinization offer potential but unproved alternatives. Bureau of Reclamation experiments suggest that winter cloud-seeding over western mountains could significantly increase the snowpack that provides the source of nearly all river flow in the region. The Interior Department estimates that weather modification on the western slopes of the Rocky Mountains could increase Colorado River flow by about one million acre-feet a year. Investigations in 12 western river basins suggest potential increases of between 7.5 million and 10 million acre-feet a year. But weather modification faces many technical, legal and environmental problems, including opposition from the residents of mountain areas who would have to cope with added snowfall.

Some western regions could increase water supplies by desalting seawater or brackish underground water. The National Water Commission concluded in 1973 that 20 years of federally supported research had perfected desalinization techniques. Some arid countries in the Middle East and

---

The Central Arizona Project

The Central Arizona Project (CAP), a key component of the Colorado River Basin Project Act of 1968, underscores the economic and political importance of western water and provides a classic case study of massive federal water projects. CAP will begin diverting Colorado River water to the Phoenix and Tucson areas by about 1985, at a cost of at least $1.4-billion. It will carry some 1.2 million acre-feet more than 300 miles, lifting it 1,000 feet above river level through a series of dams, reservoirs, pumping stations and aqueducts. But it still will not overcome an anticipated 1.8 million acre-foot groundwater shortfall in the three counties it will serve.

State and federal officials are trying to allocate CAP costs and supplies among potential water users. Critics of federal water projects are challenging CAP's financial basis and even the assumption that more water is essential to Arizona's economy. Congressional approval of the project was the result of intensive bargaining and trade-offs among delegations from the western states and powerful committee chairmen.

(For background, see Congressional Quarterly's *Congress and the Nation*, Vol. II, pp. 521-528).

---

elsewhere have begun large-scale desalting operations. Costs remain prohibitive for most American uses, particularly for agriculture, although some surveys suggest that desalted water might be competitive for small-scale municipal and industrial use.

More Efficient Uses of Western Water

The obvious alternative to augmenting water supply is using existing water resources more efficiently. The Arizona Water Commission is examining ways to reduce water use in the state. In most western states, water conservation opportunities are now available, including better irrigation techniques, industrial and agricultural recycling of municipal waste water, and urban landscaping with native desert plants instead of trees, grass and shrubs that must be watered.

Reservoir evaporation can be controlled by retardant films spread over the water surface, by storing water underground or by building smaller reservoirs higher in river watersheds. "Water harvesting" techniques can increase precipitation runoff by managing forest growth and snowpacks, by treating soils to cut moisture losses, or by curtailing the spread of phreatophytic plants. All such measures are potentially costly—although probably less expensive than most supply-augmentation plans—and may cause unforeseen environmental problems.

Far more significant water savings are possible in irrigated agriculture, which accounts for more than 80 per cent of western water depletion. Of nearly 70 million acre-feet consumed annually by irrigation in the 11 westernmost states, the Interior Department estimates that about 20 million acre-feet are lost through seepage, evaporation and consumption by natural vegetation. Farmers can cut their losses through such measures as lining ditches with concrete, timing their water deliveries better and adopting advanced irrigation techniques. The so-called "trickle" technique, which delivers water directly to individual plants at root level, potentially uses about one-fourth of the water required by conventional ditch irrigation.

Water shortages eventually could force the West to abandon much of its irrigated farming and let the desert reclaim the land. In final competition for available water, western farmers probably will be unable to withstand the pressure exerted by city dwellers and powerful energy companies. For farmers, the value of water tends to be relatively low—typically from $5 to $25 an acre-foot—because irrigation requires such large quantities and because the extra crop revenues generated by additional water are slight. In the city, however, the value of water for domestic use has been estimated at $100 an acre-foot, because the city dweller requires less water but uses it for drinking, cooking, bathing and other essential activities. Similarly, big industry has the economic power to buy whatever water it requires. But conservation could make a significant difference. "If you save 10 per cent of the water used in agriculture," Cummings noted, "you can almost double municipal and industrial uses."

Water Needs of Food, Fiber and Energy

The final recommendations of the National Water Commission included: an end to federal irrigation subsidies, tough scrutiny of proposed water transfer projects, more realistic water pricing and removal of barriers to sales of water rights. These presumably would encourage the shift of existing supplies away from agriculture. The commission questioned the economic justification for western reclamation programs while naturally productive lands lie idle in other parts of the country.

Yet resistance can be expected not only from farmers but from business interests closely tied to agriculture and from others concerned about industrialization of the West. If the nation encounters long-lasting food and fiber supply problems, the trend could even reverse itself. "If we start getting into food shortages, then water in agriculture will be a pretty good commodity," commented Carl Slingerland, staff engineer for the New Mexico Interstate Stream Commission. The same thing could happen if the United States began making greater use of agriculture to meet foreign policy objectives or to satisfy humanitarian concern about starvation abroad.

Water shortages potentially could become a common constraint on both food and energy supplies. "We've really yet to address the interface between the two crises," Cummings remarked. "Here in the Rocky Mountain chain clearly the trade-off is between agriculture and energy. Industry can buy water from agriculture; we see that happening in Arizona, Colorado and other states. We haven't asked...the question, 'Do we want that to happen?' "

Irrigation cutbacks nonetheless appear inevitable. "We've developed agriculture in the Southwest beyond its natural habitat, into unsuitable areas," Calkin said. "If it's an either-or choice, we'll send agriculture back into the areas where it quite properly belongs." Whatever the fate of irrigated agriculture, the West faces painful adjustments in the decades ahead as water shortages worsen. After a century of defying a hostile environment, westerners will have to start learning again how to live within the desert's limits.

Selected Bibliography

Books

Berkman, Richard L. and W. Kip Viscusi, *Damming the West* (Ralph Nader's Study Group Report on the Bureau of Reclamation), Grossman Publishers, 1973.

Boorstin, Daniel J., *The Americans: The National Experience*, Vintage Books, 1965.

Borgstrom, Georg, *Too Many: An Ecological Overview of Earth's Limitations*, Macmillan, 1969.

Horgan, Paul, *Great River: The Rio Grande in North American History* (2 vols.), Rinehart & Co., 1954.

Howe, Charles W. and K. William Easter, *Interbasin Transfers of Water, Economic Issues and Impacts*, Resources for the Future, 1971.

Ingram, Helen M., *Patterns of Politics in Water Resource Development: A Case Study of New Mexico's Role in the Colorado River Basin Bill*, University of New Mexico Institute for Social Research and Development, 1969.

Kelso, Maurice M., William E. Martin and Lawrence E. Mack, *Water Supplies and Economic Growth in an Arid Environment*, University of Arizona Press, 1973.

Laporte, Leo F., *Encounter With the Earth: Resources*, Harper & Row, 1975.

Nikolaieff, George A. (ed.), *The Water Crisis*, The H. W. Wilson Co., 1967.

Smith, Henry Nash, *Virgin Land: The American West as Symbol and Myth*, Harvard University Press, 1950.

Articles

"Coast to Coast—Water Becomes a Big Worry," *U.S. News & World Report*, Sept. 6, 1976.

Weatherford, Gary D. and Gordon C. Jacoby, "Impact of Energy Development on the Law of the Colorado River," *Natural Resources Journal*, January 1975.

Webb, Walter Prescott, "The American West—Perpetual Mirage," *Harper's*, May 1957.

Reports and Studies

Arizona Water Commission, "Arizona State Water Plan Inventory of Resources and Uses," July 1975.

Bureau of Reclamation, Department of the Interior, "Critical Water Problems Facing the Eleven Western States," April 1975.

Energy Research and Development Administration and Department of the Interior, "Synthetic Fuels Commercialization Program, Draft Environmental Impact Statement," December 1975.

Editorial Research Reports, "Rural Migration," 1975 Vol. II, p. 590; "World Weather Trends," 1974 Vol. II, p. 515; "Oil Shale Development," 1968 Vol. II, p. 905; "Water Resources and National Water Needs," 1965 Vol. II, p. 583.

National Water Commission, "Water Policies for the Future—Final Report to the President and to the Congress of the United States," June 1973.

New Mexico Water Quality Control Commission, "Southern High Plains Water Quality Management Plan," April 13, 1976.

ALASKAN DEVELOPMENT

by

John Hamer

**Dec. 17
1 9 7 6**

ALASKAN DEVELOPMENT

A LASKA means "the great land." It is indeed a state of superlatives. Alaska is larger than the next three largest states combined. It has more timber, water and copper than the rest of the United States. There may be as much oil and natural gas in Alaska and off its coasts as in all the other 49 states. Alaska has three million lakes, several major river systems, a dozen peaks higher than any other American mountains, and numerous mammoth glaciers. Alaska's fish, wildlife, plants and flowers are abundant and many are unique to the state. Yet most of Alaska still is wilderness—of the state's 375 million acres only about 100,000 acres now are taken up by cities, towns, villages, roads or other marks of human activity. It has the fewest people of any state (405,000) and the most land per resident (925 acres).

Alaska today is a state of change and turmoil. The trans-Alaska oil pipeline—perhaps the largest private construction project ever undertaken—is nearly finished, and it already has altered Alaska profoundly. The pipeline has brought millions of dollars and thousands of people to the state, creating a "boom" atmosphere unseen since the gold rush days. It remains to be seen if a "bust" will follow. There are several competing plans to build another pipeline from Alaska's North Slope to carry its enormous natural gas reserves to market *(see p. 165)*. If the "haul road" that parallels the oil pipeline north of the Yukon River is opened up to the public, the northern half of the state will be significantly affected *(see map)*. As for the southern part of the state, Alaskans voted in November to move their capital from Juneau, in the southeastern panhandle, to a new site near the tiny town of Willow, just north of Anchorage and nearer the bulk of the state's population. On the site, a new city will be built so the capital can be moved by 1980.

Much of Alaska's 586,000 square miles of land also is undergoing change of ownership. When Alaska became a state in 1959, more than 99 per cent of the land was owned by the federal government. Today the government is in the midst of a complicated process of turning some land over to the residents of the state and setting aside other lands for preservation as national parks or monuments, national forests, wildlife refuges, scenic reserves or for other purposes. Under the Alaska Native Claims Settlement Act, passed by Congress five years ago, 40 million acres are to be turned over to the state's Eskimos, Aleuts and Indians; up to 80 million additional acres will be set aside in the national interest. This process is to be completed by December 1978, and a myriad of difficult questions remain to be decided *(see p. 154).*

For all of these reasons, the future of Alaskan development still is clouded by uncertainty. It has been said that there are three types of people in Alaska—those who are pro-development and want to see great progress as quickly as feasible, those who are anti-development and want to preserve the state in its natural condition as much as possible, and those who are somewhere in the middle and prefer a cautious approach favoring careful development. Several years ago, author Richard Austin Smith wrote "[Alaska is] a treasure house of natural resources—fish, timber, minerals, oil—but the hostility of nature and the high cost of development prevent orderly exploitation. It goes by fits and starts."[1] It is still that way in Alaska. More development in the nation's 49th state is inevitable, but the nature and quality of that development remain to be determined.

Gov. Jay Hammond, a Republican elected in 1974 on a platform endorsing prudent, balanced development, said in his 1976 State of the State address: "Of course, growth and change are foreordained—some good, some bad, and to maximize the good will take careful orchestration. ...[W]e wish to steer growth, not strangle it, unless, of course, it cannot pay its way."[2]

Profound Effects of the Alaska Oil Pipeline

The trans-Alaska oil pipeline is the kind of project that has aroused endless debate over whether it represents healthy or unhealthy growth. Enormous investments in time, money, resources and people have been poured into the pipeline over the past few years. Some of them clearly will result in long-term economic benefits for Alaska and the nation, while others have raised questions about their ultimate social and environmental impact on the state. The 800-mile-long, 48-inch diameter steel pipeline, extending from the North Slope oilfields to the port of Valdez on the Gulf of Alaska, is now about 97 per cent complete. Pumping stations and terminal facilities are more than 80 per cent complete.[3]

Alyeska Pipeline Service Co., a consortium of companies that

[1] Richard Austin Smith, *The Frontier States—Alaska, Hawaii* (1968), p. 18.
[2] Quoted from text of address, *Anchorage Times,* Jan. 19, 1976.
[3] For a detailed discussion of the current status of the pipeline, see *Congressional Quarterly Weekly Report,* Nov. 27, 1976, pp. 3241-3248.

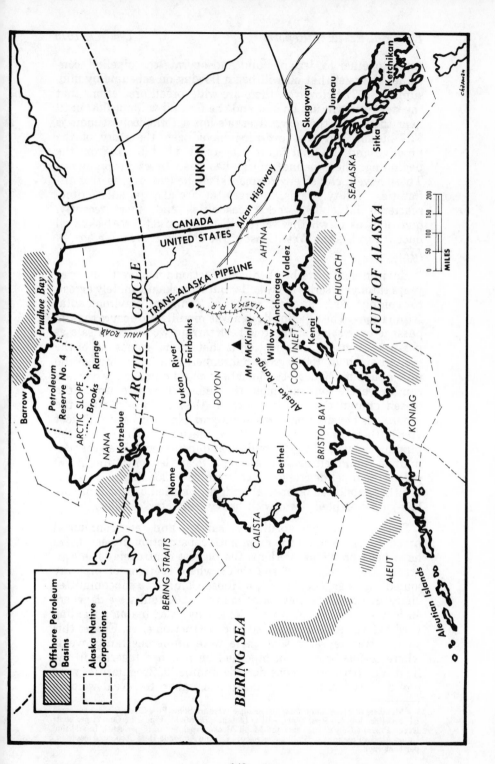

149

came together to design, build and operate the pipeline, continues to insist that oil will begin flowing on schedule by midsummer 1977.[4] However, there are widespread predictions that the deadline will not be met and the first oil will not flow until near the end of the year. Alyeska's latest total cost estimate is $7.7-billion, but cost overruns have been the story of the pipeline and the final figure may reach $10-billion. From the beginning, the pipeline project has been beset by problems. These have included environmental challenges, engineering difficulties, faulty welds, charges of fraud, sporadic crime, scattered oil spills, worker casualties and, most recently, questions as to whether there will be a market for Alaskan oil once it reaches the West Coast of the United States *(see box, p. 157).*

Environmentalists blocked construction for more than three years through a series of lawsuits, but Alyeska ultimately agreed to comply with a wide range of stringent environmental stipulations. The pipeline design was modified to ensure that its passage over some of the roughest terrain would be as safe as possible. A major complication is that the oil comes out of the ground at about 180 degrees Fahrenheit and flows through the pipe at about 140 degrees. Such heat could damage the delicate tundra vegetation and melt the underlying permafrost, the frozen ground that covers most of Alaska. For 425 miles the pipeline is elevated on vertical support platforms about 60 feet apart; there are more than 78,000 platforms. The rest of the pipeline is buried 3 to 12 feet deep and insulated to keep the permafrost from melting and causing it to settle or rupture. In 800 places the pipeline crosses river, streams or floodplains, where it is either supported on special bridges or buried beneath the surface and weighted down with heavy concrete "saddles."

Despite the extraordinary safety and environmental precautions taken on the mammoth construction project, there have been problems. Perhaps the biggest controversy has concerned the integrity of the welds where sections of pipe are joined together. On Dec. 11, a House Commerce subcommittee charged that there may be as many as 200 faulty welds where 40-foot sections of pipe were joined by machine at a welding yard before being transported to construction sites. Earlier this year it was revealed that there were numerous faulty welds where 80-foot sections of pipe had been joined together in the field. Furthermore, a considerable number of irregularities were found in the X-rays, or radiographs, taken to reveal welding

[4] Members of Alyeska and their ownership shares are Sohio Pipe Line Co. (33.3 per cent), BP Pipelines Inc. (15.8 per cent), ARCO [Atlantic Richfield] Pipe Line Co. (21 per cent), Exxon Pipeline Co. (20 per cent) and Mobil Alaska Pipeline Co. (5 per cent). In addition, Union Alaska Pipeline Co., Phillips Petroleum Co. and Amerada Hess Corp. hold less than 2 per cent each.

Where Will Alaska's Oil Go?

The biggest question about Alaskan oil today is: Where will it go? If transported to the U.S. West Coast, it will be a glut on the market. Eastern and midwestern states sorely need the oil but are far from West Coast ports.

When the pipeline construction began, it was assumed that the oil could be absorbed in the western states. But reduced growth of energy demands, the opening of California's Elk Hills Naval Petroleum Reserve and increased imports from Indonesia have led to an overabundant supply of oil on the West Coast. By 1978, when 1.2 million barrels a day are flowing through the Alaska pipeline, the surplus may total 500,000 barrels a day.

There are several plans for handling the potential surplus. Sohio, which controls one-third of the North Slope reserves, wants to build a terminal at Long Beach, Calif., and a 200-mile pipeline to link with an existing but unused natural gas pipeline that runs to Midland, Texas, where refineries and other pipeline hookups are located. The biggest obstacle is the objection of California officials to air pollution they expect to result from the unloading of oil tankers at Long Beach.

Other companies have proposed northern pipeline routes to the midwestern states. One envisions a terminal near Kitimat, British Columbia, and an 800-mile pipeline to connect to existing lines at Edmonton, Alberta, and then to U.S. lines. Another would involve building a 1,500-mile pipeline from a proposed terminal at Port Angeles, Wash., to Clearbrook, Minn. But all of these facilities are costly and could not be operating until 1979 at the earliest. Several companies have proposed shipping the excess oil by tanker through the Panama Canal and up the Gulf of Mexico to refineries and pipeline centers in the South. But this, too, would be costly and would require a fleet of tankers small enough to transit the canal. It also might necessitate waiver of the Jones Act, which requires that U.S. oil be shipped to U.S. ports on ships built, owned and crewed by Americans.

Finally, some oil company executives and government officials have proposed selling Alaskan oil to Japan in exchange for diverting Middle Eastern oil, now purchased by Japan, to the U.S. East Coast. This swap would save both countries millions of dollars in shipping costs. But it would require an act of Congress, since the 1973 Alaska Pipeline bill specifically prohibited the export of Alaskan oil except in extraordinary circumstances.

flaws. There were also charges that some X-rays were falsified, unreadable or missing. After an audit of 30,800 welds, Alyeska disclosed 3,955 deficiencies and agreed to correct them all. By early December, according to federal officials, only 31 welds remained to be repaired. But criticism and controversy persist.

Environmentalists contend that the emphasis on rapid construction had sacrificed environmental rules. The Fairbanks

Environmental Center recently issued a 92-page report documenting allegations of environmental abuse and poor federal oversight during construction. The report cited a lack of erosion control, inadequate protection of fish and wildlife, violations of water-quality standards, and deliberate oil discharges.[5] And it said there has been little enforcement, corrective or legal action by federal inspectors.

A fear of all who are involved is that an earthquake might someday rupture the pipeline, which crosses three major earthquake zones. Alyeska's design supposedly will allow the pipe to whip 20 feet from side to side and five feet up and down without breaking. The company has said the pipeline could survive earthquakes that measure up to 8.5 on the Richter scale. The severest earthquake ever recorded in Alaska—the 1964 tremor that destroyed much of Anchorage and all of Valdez—measured between 8.3 and 8.6. A series of electronic sensors along the pipeline will detect oil pressure drops as slight as 1 per cent, and technicians at remote-control stations can then close off the affected segment in minutes. Alyeska believes it can hold any leaks to less than 50,000 barrels, while critics contend that much larger spills could go undetected for days. Another fear is of an oil-tanker accident in the treacherous Prince William Sound near Valdez, where foggy and windy weather conditions prevail, or in the stormy Gulf of Alaska off the state's southern coast.

State Government Concern Over Oil Royalties

But if the oil pipeline has negative effects on Alaska's environment, it clearly will have positive effects on the state's treasury. When oil was discovered on the North Slope in 1968, the state sold oil and gas leases on 451,000 acres for $900-million. But eight years later it had nearly used up the money and was forced to sell more leases to remain solvent. It also levied a "reserve tax" on oil deposits and a property tax on the pipeline and related facilities. Alaska still owns the land it leased and is due to receive a 12.5 per cent royalty on the wellhead value of the oil produced at Prudhoe Bay. So the first year the pipeline becomes operational, the state estimates it will collect $480-million in royalties and taxes. By 1980 the amount could increase to $1-billion a year, if the pipeline production schedule holds up, and to $2-billion by 1984.

The exact amount the state receives, however, will be computed by a complex formula that involves a still-undetermined tariff on the North Slope oil. The state royalties will be based on the market value of oil at the wellhead minus the tariff. The

[5] G.M. Zemansky, "Environmental Non-Compliance and the Public Interest During Construction of the Trans-Alaska Pipeline," September 1976.

tariff, to be set by the Interstate Commerce Commission, includes the costs of pipeline construction, amortization fees, operation and maintenance expenses, and related costs. So the higher the ultimate cost of the pipeline, the lower the state's royalties and revenues. The Alaska Department of Revenue has calculated that when the flow of oil reaches 1.2 million barrels a day, a difference of just one cent in the tariff per barrel would mean a gain or loss of more than $1-million in state income.

The matter is so crucial that the state recently hired a former Senate Watergate Committee lawyer, Terry F. Lenzner, to investigate cost overruns on the pipeline project. Lenzner was hired by the Alaska Pipeline Commission, a three-member panel formed by the governor in 1972 to protect state interests. If poor management, negligence, bad workmanship, low productivity, lack of quality control or fraud are identified as having increased pipeline costs, the state will try to reduce the amount used to calculate the tariff. There have been doubts in the past that the state had the leadership, money, personnel and will to negotiate successfully with the oil companies. Several state officials have gone to work for the companies, including a former attorney general who is now an Alyeska lobbyist, Norman Gorsuch. But the stakes in the royalties issues are enormous, and the state is expected to fight for all it can get.

Social Impact of Huge Construction Project

The most visible effects of the pipeline are social and economic. The project at its peak created jobs for 21,000 workers, most of whom came in from outside the state, including many pipeline welders from Texas and Oklahoma. Thousands more flocked to Alaska hoping to find high-paying jobs on the pipeline but often ending up broke and stranded. The population of Fairbanks, the main staging area for the project, increased by more than 25 per cent, while that of Valdez more than quadrupled. Pipeline employment is falling rapidly, as it has every winter, but there will be no buildup next spring.

Even so, the pipeline has left a legacy that will never disappear. Ron Rau, a pipeline worker and free-lance writer, called it "the taming of Alaska." He wrote: "In many ways, the pipeline is like an iceberg. What you see with your eyes is only a fraction of what is really there. The real threat to the Alaskan wilderness and life-style is the part of the pipeline you cannot see: the money, the people and, most of all, the boom-town mentality that has permeated Alaskan society—a warm, modern house, a steady job and two snowmobiles in every garrage."[6]

[6] Ron Rau, "The Taming of Alaska," *National Wildlife*, October-November 1976, pp. 19-20.

The sudden spurt in development also had some more serious side effects—increases in crime, prostitution, gambling, alcoholism, venereal disease, divorce and child neglect. "This is no boom," former Fairbanks Mayor Sylvia Ringstadt has said. "It's a boomerang."[7] Mim Dixon of the Pipeline Impact Information Center in Fairbanks, an organization dedicated to keeping track of the project's social costs, said: "There's a real disregard for the human cost. They're trying to build the pipeline as fast as they can.... But the way the project is structured there's incredible stress on families and the community and not many benefits."[8] Fairbanks also has suffered housing shortages, traffic congestion, overburdened city services, crowded schools, and rampant inflation. Fairbanks, more than any other place, probably will feel the "boom-and-bust" effects of the pipeline for years.

Status of the Native Land Claims Settlement

What may have even greater long-range impact on Alaska than the pipeline is the Alaska Native Claims Settlement Act. Passed by Congress in 1971, it gave the state's approximately 60,000 Eskimos, Indians and Aleuts 40 million acres of land, and $962.5-million payable over several years. Of the money, $462.5-million was in direct federal grants and up to $500-million is to come from a 2 per cent royalty on mineral revenues derived from state and federal lands. The land is being apportioned by a complex formula that established 12 regional corporations, divided geographically on roughly ethnic lines, and about 220 village corporations. The villages were given surface rights to a total of 22 million acres of land that surround existing villages. The regional corporations were granted mineral rights to the village lands, plus full title (surface and underground rights) to the rest of the 40 million acres.

It was by far the largest settlement ever made by the U.S. government with any group of North American natives. The idea was to give the natives the greatest possible role in determining their own future. They were given full control over their lands and enough money to make investments to provide for the future. Peter J. Schuyten wrote in *Fortune* magazine: "Thrusting the loosely organized Alaskan natives into the corporate world might seem somewhat analogous to sending Henry Ford II out in a walrus-skinned canoe in charge of an Eskimo whaling expedition." But to the surprise of many, the native corporations have turned out to be remarkably aggressive and successful experiments in minority capitalism. They have invested in nearly every segment of the Alaskan economy—

---

[7] Quoted in *Time,* June 2, 1975, p. 20.
[8] Quoted by Michael Roberts, "Dissolute Alaska," *The New Republic,* Nov. 1, 1975, p. 18.

Crime in Alaska

For more than a year, allegations have circulated that Alaska—as a result of the pipeline project—is plagued by widespread lawlessness, rampant thievery, organized crime, union bossism and official helplessness in dealing with the problems. The charges were primarily the result of a series of stories appearing in the *Los Angeles Times* in November 1975 that sought to document "a runaway crime wave" in the state.

The *Times* quoted Gov. Jay Hammond as saying that Alaska's top Teamster boss, Jesse L. Carr, had grown so powerful that "nobody is going to challenge him." It quoted state Attorney General Avrum M. Gross saying of Alyeska Pipe Line Company: "They'll do nothing to provoke the unions. They just want to finish that line." And it quoted Alyeska President E. L. Patton as saying he was sure that "there's been more stuff stolen from this project than in the whole history of Alaska."

However, after initial praise for the stories, including compliments from state officials who were quoted, grumblings began to surface that the reporting was inaccurate or exaggerated. Other newspapers portrayed the situation in Alaska as not quite so bad. Teamster chief Carr called the *Times* account "fiction."

The *Times* stuck by its stories, and in December 1975 it reported that a federal Law Enforcement Assistance Administration official had come to the same conclusions about crime in Alaska and had recommended a large grant to help fight lawlessness. In 1976, nine persons were indicted by a federal grand jury in Alaska on charges of conspiring to run prostitution and gambling rings along the pipeline. Two of them were former high state officials. And in November, Attorney General Gross said he expected to convene a state grand jury early in 1977 to investigate organized crime.

banking, mineral and oil exploration, construction, real estate, logging, hotel management, fishing and reindeer herding.[9]

One of the largest regional corporations, Doyon, Ltd., has about 9,200 stockholders, mostly Athabascan Indians. It has a partnership with Louisiana Land & Exploration Co. to drill for oil along the Yukon River, a joint venture with ASARCO, Inc.,[10] to prospect for asbestos, and a contract to maintain the pipeline haul road with Alaska International Construction. Another, the Bristol Bay Corp., purchased Peter Pan Seafoods of Seattle for $9-million, entered into a joint venture with Phillips Petroleum Co. to drill for oil on corporation land, and pooled funds with four other native corporations to start the state-chartered United Bank of Alaska. Calista Corp. has begun building a $25-

---

[9] "A Novel Corporation Takes Charge in Alaska's Wilderness," *Fortune*, October 1975, p. 158.

[10] Formerly the American Smelting and Refining Co.

million hotel in Anchorage that will be managed by Sheraton. "The natives are becoming businessmen and Republicans," said Jack Ferguson, administrative assistant to Rep. Don Young (R Alaska). "They're beginning to think more like Chamber of Commerce members than tribal hunters."

There have been some problems. The 1971 act provided that each regional corporation must share 70 per cent of its mineral revenues with the others so that all natives would benefit from lands rich in oil, coal or other minerals. But the act did not specify if that meant *gross* or *net* revenues. The result has been a tangle of litigation, with corporations suing each other to determine which gets what and how much. Also, about 18,000 natives eligible to share in the act's benefits were no longer living in Alaska. For legal purposes, any person with one-quarter native blood is considered a native.

Court action and subsequent legislation created a 13th regional corporation for natives living outside of Alaska. They must register by Jan. 2, 1977, or lose their chance to claim shares. Also, in 1991—20 years after the effective date of the act—the natives will be able to sell their shares in the corporations and the land they manage will become taxable for the first time. There is some fear that this will lead to widespread efforts by unscrupulous buyers to gain control of the natives' holdings.

Selection of 'D-2' National Interest Lands

Another current development destined to have an enormous long-term impact on Alaska is the selection of land under section 17(d)(2) of the 1971 act, commonly referred to as the "D-2 lands." That section directed the Secretary of the Interior to recommend up to 80 million acres of the unallocated federal lands in Alaska for designation as national parks, national forests, wildlife refuges or wild and scenic rivers. Within five years of the Secretary's recommendations, Congress was directed to establish the areas officially and set their boundaries.

A task force composed of representatives from the National Park Service, Forest Service, Fish and Wildlife Service and Bureau of Outdoor Recreation spent most of two years combing Alaska for the most important wildlife, scenic, recreational and historic areas. The results were made public in December 1973, when Secretary of the Interior Rogers C. B. Morton submitted to Congress proposals for the withdrawal of 28 parks, refuges and other units totaling about 83 million acres. Predictably, pro-development interests promptly accused Morton of trying to "lock up" too many valuable resources from exploitation while some environmentalists objected that Morton had not recommended enough lands to be preserved for posterity.

In the past three years, at least half a dozen bills have been introduced in Congress containing specific proposals for the D-2 lands. Their acreage recommendations range from about 64 million up to some 106 million. In addition to the Interior Department's proposal, major bills have been introduced by Reps. Don Young (R Alaska), Morris K. Udall (D Ariz.), John D. Dingell (D Mich.) and by Sen. Henry M. Jackson (D Wash.). And the state has prepared its own proposal, which suggests reducing the amount of land set aside into the four traditional federal management areas while creating new categories of "Alaska resources land" and "cooperative management areas." The idea of a "fifth system" of national interest reserves also has been presented in some of the bills in Congress.

In the meantime, a federal-state Land Use Planning Commission created by the 1971 act has been meeting regularly over the past few years, and with the help of a full-time staff has been making recommendations for resolution of the complex D-2 lands issue. The commission has four members appointed by the governor of Alaska, four members by the Secretary of the Interior and one member by the President. According to the act, the commission's purpose is to ensure that Alaska's economic growth is "orderly, planned and compatible with state and national environmental objectives, the public interest in the public lands...and the economic and social well-being of the native people and other residents of Alaska."

Slow Progress of Past Development

THE FIRST human settlement of the land now known as Alaska came thousands of years ago, probably when primitive tribes crossed the ancient "land bridge" that joined Asia to North America. The Eskimos and other Indians adapted to the harsh climate both physically and psychologically, developing a great tolerance for cold weather. The first white explorers in the area fared less well —in 1741 Vitus Bering, a Dane sailing in the service of Russia, was shipwrecked in a winter storm and died along with most of his crew. Nonetheless, he is credited with the "discovery" of Alaska. Several survivors of the Bering expedition returned to Russia in a rebuilt ship. They included a naturalist named Georg Steller who described in great

Alaskan Historic Highlights

1741. "Discovery" by Vitus Bering for Russia.

1867. Purchase of Alaska by United States for $7.2-million.

1884. First Organic Act and appointment of governor.

1896-1900. Klondike gold rush in Yukon and Nome gold strike.

1903. Alaskan Boundary Award to settle U.S.-Canadian border.

1906. Congress authorized a non-voting delegate from Alaska.

1912. Alaska granted territorial status.

1923. Alaska Railroad completed.

1940-1943. U.S. military buildup in Alaska; battle of Attu.

1958. Statehood measure passed by Congress.

1959. Alaska official became a state.

1964. Good Friday earthquake hit Anchorage and Gulf Coast.

1968. Oil and natural gas discovered at Prudhoe Bay.

1971. Alaska Native Land Claims Settlement Act approved.

1973. Alaska oil pipeline bill approved.

detail the seals, sea otters and other animals whose luxurious furs helped enable the sailors to survive the rigors of the Arctic cold.

Within two years, the first Alaskan "boom" had begun—the fur trade. Hardy Siberian *promyshleniki*—fur hunters—followed the Aleutian Islands to the Alaska mainland, harvesting thousands of marine mammals along the way. When one hunting ground was depleted, the hunters moved on. If the local Aleut tribesmen objected, they were enslaved or shot; thousands were killed within a few years in the latter half of the 18th century. But greedy exploitation by the Russians brought many fur-bearing animal species near extinction, and the fur hunters' profits eventually began to fall.

In 1776 the British Admiralty sent Captain James Cook up the Alaskan coast to look for a Northwest Passage, with secret instructions to claim any unsettled lands in the name of the Crown. Cook did so, but the Russians went right on establishing seaports, towns and fortifications all along the coast. In 1804 the Russian government granted exclusive rights to Alaskan exploitation to a commercial enterprise, the Russian-American Co., which gradually extended its holdings as far south as California. "The real significance of the Russian-American regime in the pageant of history was that by it Alaska was transferred to the sovereignty of the United States," Ernest

Gruening wrote in his influential book, *The State of Alaska* (1954). "Russia's occupation began just in time to forestall Britain's. But for Russia, Alaska would today be a province of Canada."[11]

The Russian presence in North America lasted for 126 years. The Russians realized during the Crimean War (1853-56) that their naval power was inadequate and they probably could not hold their North American outposts. Not long after the American Civil War ended, word reached U.S. Secretary of State William Henry Seward that the Russians wanted to sell Alaska. Seward had coveted the vast Alaskan territory for several years, and he immediately began negotiations with Baron Eduard Stoeckel, Russian Minister to the United States, to draft a treaty of cession. On March 30, 1867, the treaty was signed. It was ratified by Congress a few months later despite grumblings by skeptics that "Walrussia" was a worthless and icebound land. Nonetheless, Congress later appropriated $7.2-million for the purchase—less than two cents an acre. The ceremony officially transferring ownership was held Oct. 18, 1867, in Sitka—the Russian capital in North America and one of the few places where evidence of their domain still may be found. "Seward's Folly" was in American hands.

Years of Neglect Following U.S. Purchase

The event was followed by a long period of neglect. "[T]he distant government in Washington seemingly forgot about the new purchase," Bern Keating wrote in *Alaska* (1971). The territory was variously under the jurisdiction of the Army, the Navy and the Treasury Departments, and official policies were vague and contradictory. Geologist and explorer William H. Dall wrote that Alaska was "a country where no man could make a legal will, own a homestead...or so much as cut wood for his fire without defying a congressional prohibition; where polygamy and slavery and the lynching of witches prevailed, with no legal authority to stay or punish criminals."[12] In 1884 the first Organic Act gave Alaska some laws and a governor was appointed.

Then in 1896, gold was discovered in the Canadian Yukon. Thousands of prospectors moved through the Alaskan port of Skagway, just over the Coast Mountains from Whitehorse, where the headwaters of the Yukon River and the road to the Klondike began. The discovery also touched off a dispute between the United States and Canada over Alaska's eastern

---

[11] *The State of Alaska*, p. 3. Gruening was governor of the Territory of Alaska from 1939-53 and one of the state's first two U.S. senators from 1959-69.

[12] Quoted by Richard Austin Smith in *The Frontier States—Alaska, Hawaii* (1968), pp. 15-16.

Alaskan Facts and Figures

Area. 586,412 square miles, larger than Texas, California and Montana combined.

Shore line. 33,904 miles, about 38 per cent of the total U.S. shore line.

Continental Shelf. 560,000 square miles, about 65 per cent of total U.S. continental shelf.

Climate. Relatively mild and wet in southern parts of state; extremes of summer and winter temperatures in central regions; Arctic climate on North Slope.

Time Zones. Four—Pacific, Yukon, Alaska and Bering.

Major Resources. Oil, natural gas, fisheries, timber, copper, gold, coal, iron, water.

Population. Approximately 405,000 in 1975, including 60,-000 resident native Eskimos, Aleuts and Indians, according to state estimates.

Capital. Juneau, to be changed to Willow by 1980.

Governor. Jay Hammond (R), elected to four-year term in 1974.

State Legislature. 40-member House of Representatives, 20-member Senate.

boundary, never defined by the Russians. The Canadians wanted a line that generally followed the ocean's edge, while the United States preferred a line that dipped in and out with the many bays and inlets of Alaska's southeastern panhandle. After several years of inconclusive argument, Great Britain suggested that the matter be settled by a British-American panel, and Canada reluctantly agreed. The resulting Alaskan Boundary Award was so favorable to the United States that Canada initially refused to sign it.

Other gold discoveries on the Seward Peninsula had brought 20,000 adventurers to the new boom town of Nome in 1899. This briefly drew the attention of the U.S. government to Alaska. In 1900 provisions were made to incorporate the most populous towns, and Juneau was designated the capital. In 1906 Congress authorized a non-voting delegate from Alaska, and in 1912 a territorial government was established. Efforts to open up Alaska for resource development by large corporations aroused conservationists during Theodore Roosevelt's administration, and they campaigned to set aside large areas for posterity. Enormous amounts of land were preserved as national parks, national monuments, national forests or wildlife refuges, while other areas became military reservations, bombing ranges, water-conservation districts, road rights-of-way or mineral preserves. In 1923 the Navy and the Interior Departments withdrew about one-twelfth of Alaska's land as Petroleum Reserve Number 4, or "Pet 4," closing it to private exploration.

There were scattered appeals for more Alaskan home rule in the early 1900s, and the first statehood bill was introduced in Congress in 1916. But for the most part, Keating wrote, "the Great Land continued to doze in virtual hibernation till World War II." With Japan threatening in the Pacific, U.S. forces in Alaska were built up to nearly 150,000 troops. In 1943, they fought a fierce battle to retake the island of Attu, at the tip of the Aleutian chain, which had been occupied by the Japanese. It was the war's only ground fighting in North America, and although nearly forgotten today, ranks second to the assault on Iwo Jima as the nation's most costly battle in the ratio of American to Japanese casualties.[13]

Lengthy Campaign to Win Alaskan Statehood

After the war ended, agitation for Alaskan statehood began to increase. Ernest Gruening, who had been appointed territorial governor in 1939, became a strong proponent of statehood. In *The Battle for Alaska Statehood* (1967), Gruening wrote that as governor: "[I began to realize] the revenues derived from Alaska's resources were virtually negligible. Alaska was in the grip of absentee interests and had been for a quarter of a century. They were violently opposed to any taxation that would lessen their profits or in any way interfere with their desire to take as much from Alaska as quickly as possible.... By 1945 I

---

[13] For every 100 Japanese casualties, 71 U.S. soldiers were killed or wounded on Attu.

realized that Alaska's territorial status burdened it with insuperable handicaps and that statehood was essential."[14]

The territorial legislature approved a pro-statehood resolution in 1945 and placed a statehood referendum on the 1946 election ballot. Alaskan voters responded by endorsing statehood, 9,630 to 6,822. "While the majority was not overwhelming," Gruening wrote, "the three to two vote was understandable because of the long-standing opposition propaganda of the really controlling forces—the absentee interests." The Alaska Statehood Association was formed and its members began to seek support for their cause throughout the territory and in Washington, D.C. An influential ally was President Truman, who spoke in favor of statehood in his first State of the Union message. However, President Eisenhower, in his first State of the Union message, endorsed statehood for Hawaii while omitting any mention of Alaska. During much of the 1950s, Alaskan statehood was opposed in Congress by a coalition of Republicans and Southern Democrats. But after lengthy hearings in the nation's capital and in various cities in Alaska, sentiment favoring statehood gradually grew stronger.

The territorial legislature voted in 1955 to hold a constitutional convention to force the statehood issue. "In all, the constitution was a model of clarity, brevity and strength, and it seemed to speak well of Alaskans' political maturity," Neal R. Peirce wrote in *The Pacific States of America* (1972). Also, statehood backers decided to try the "Tennessee Plan" of sending two "shadow" senators and a representative to Washington, D.C., to lobby for statehood.[15]

Eisenhower and his Secretary of the Interior, Fred A. Seaton, endorsed statehood in 1958 and the Alaska Statehood Bill passed the House of Representatives on May 28 that year by a vote of 210 to 166, and the Senate on June 30 by a 64-20 vote. Eisenhower signed the measure into law on July 7, and later that summer Alaskan voters accepted statehood by an overwhelming 5-1 majority. Alaska officially became a state on Jan. 3, 1959. The long battle for Alaskan statehood had been won.

Native Land Claims Issue and Pipeline Approval

When Alaska achieved statehood, the federal government still owned more than 99 per cent of the state's land. The statehood act gave Alaska the right to "select" for its own use 103 million

---

[14] Ernest Gruening, *The Battle for Alaska Statehood* (1967), pp. 1-2.

[15] The plan is thus named because the Territory of Tennessee followed it in 1796 and gained statehood within a few months. The Alaskan delegation consisted of Gruening, William Egan, who later became the state's first governor, and Ralph J. Rivers, who became the first U.S. representative. Gruening and Bob Bartlett, who had been the territorial delegate since 1945, became U.S. senators.

acres of the 375 million acres in federal control. But the law also said the state should "forever disclaim all right and title...to any lands or other property (including fishing rights)...which may be held by Eskimos, Indians or Aleuts." So when the state began to exercise its authority to select acreage, it encountered vehement protest from natives who believed they had ancestral rights to millions of acres. "Natives began to file stupendous land claims, overlapping both federally held public domain as well as state-selected land and including, significantly, the billion-dollar oil lands of the North Slope," Peirce wrote.[16] Late in 1966, Secretary of the Interior Stewart L. Udall imposed a freeze on all further federal land transfers until Congress settled the native land claims issue.

That same year, the native population unified for the first time under the statewide Alaskan Federation of Natives (AFN), which became increasingly forceful in arguing for a just settlement of the dispute. "The land is our life," argued Donald Wright, an Athabascan Indian who was AFN president. "Take our land—take our life!"[17] The Alaska Native Claims Settlement Act was cleared by Congress in December 1971 after a lengthy lobbying campaign.[18] Actually, some credit passage of the Alaska Native Claims Act to the 1968 oil discoveries on Alaska's North Slope. The oil companies wanted a quick settlement of the native lands issue so they could proceed with oilfield development and pipeline construction. "The justice of our cause, mixed with oil—that's what did it," said Edward L. Weinberg, an attorney for the natives, of the 1971 law's passage.

When Alaska gained statehood, it picked two million acres on the North Slope, between the Brooks Range and the Beaufort Sea in the Arctic Ocean, as part of its selections of federal lands. For decades Eskimos had used oil seepages there for fuel, and petroleum geologists suspected that oil-bearing structures might lie below the surface. As early as 1963, Atlantic Richfield and British Petroleum had bought leases to search for oil, but each had spent millions and found nothing. Then on Feb. 18, 1968, an Atlantic Richfield crew on a drilling rig in Prudhoe Bay struck it big. The oil and natural gas deposits later proved to be the largest single strike ever made in North America.

However, a group of environmental organizations in April 1970 began a series of lawsuits that asked for changes in the pipeline planning in order to protect the Alaskan environment. In 1972 the Interior Department gave its approval after an exhaustive study of the pipeline's environmental impact, but construction was held up pending the outcome of court challenges.

[16] Neal R. Peirce, *The Pacific States of America* (1972), p. 298.
[17] Quoted by Peirce, p. 299.
[18] For details, see *Congressional Quarterly 1971 Almanac, pp. 828-834.*

Congress finally resolved the pipeline debate in November 1973 by passing legislation that required the Secretary of the Interior to authorize construction, barred further court challenges on environmental grounds, and eased right-of-way limitations that had led to the legal delays. A crucial vote, prohibiting further court action under the National Environmental Policy Act of 1969, was won by pipeline supporters when Vice President Spiro T. Agnew cast his vote to break a 49-49 tie in the Senate.[19]

With this bill's passage, the great Alaskan oil rush was on. Summing up the history of Alaska, John McPhee wrote recently in *The New Yorker:* "A high proportion of the white people who have tried to make their way in Alaska have lived from boom to boom. The first boom was fur, and then came gold, followed by war, and now oil."[20]

Major Questions Facing the State

THE FUTURE of Alaskan development will depend on how successfully the state can satisfy a wide range of conflicting demands and interests, both public and private. In his 1976 State of the State address, Governor Hammond declared: "Our determination is to tune government to the needs of the people; not tinker with it to the tune of special interests." He continued: "To simplify, consider the state an investment corporation and all Alaskans stockholders. We support healthy growth which will increase net corporate assets, but we will oppose unhealthy growth which costs, both economically and otherwise, the majority of stockholders in order that a few can make a handsome profit."

But distinguishing between healthy and unhealthy growth, and negotiating between special interests and the public interest, can be a tricky business. Alaska's abundant resources will continue to lure large corporations as well as individual entrepreneurs, while the state's awesome beauty still will attract people who want to see most of Alaska remain in a natural condition. There are extremists on both sides, making the task of reconciling differences more difficult. And because Alaska is apparently the nation's greatest storehouse of fossil-fuel resources, many more Americans than the 405,000 Alaskans will be affected by decisions made in the state. "The federal program to develop energy resources on public lands may mean development whether Alaskans want it or not, and that develop-

---

[19] For details, see *Congressional Quarterly 1973 Almanac*, pp. 596-614.

[20] John McPhee, "What They were Hunting For—I," *The New Yorker*, Sept. 27, 1976, p. 81.

ment may threaten things that Alaskans value," stated a recent National Science Foundation report. "Alaska, the nation's last frontier, may be turning out to be a proving ground for the nation's ability to reconcile economic growth with a concern for human and environmental values."[21]

Natural Gas Pipeline and Offshore Leasing

One of the next major decisions affecting Alaskan development will concern how best to make the state's enormous natural gas supplies available to the rest of the nation. Proved reserves[22] of natural gas in Alaska amount to about 26 trillion cubic feet, or about 10 per cent of current U.S. requirements. But total Alaskan reserves are estimated at more than 450 trillion cubic feet—a highly desirable stockpile considering that natural gas is the fossil fuel in shortest supply in the "Lower 48" states. There are three competing proposals to pipe or ship Alaskan natural gas to U.S. markets:

1. *El Paso Natural Gas Co.* proposes to build an 800-mile pipeline parallel to the Alaska oil pipeline, then to liquefy the gas and ship it 1,900 miles south to California aboard special LNG (liquefied natural gas) tankers, where it would be regasified and pumped through existing pipeline networks. Estimated cost: $7.9-billion.

2. *Alaskan Arctic Gas Pipeline Co.,* a consortium of 15 American and Canadian companies, would build a 4,200-mile pipeline from Prudhoe Bay eastward through Canada's Mackenzie River Valley (where it would pick up Canadian natural gas), then southward through the Northwest Territories into Alberta to connect with existing U.S. and Canadian pipelines. Estimated cost: $8.3-billion.

3. *Northwest Pipeline Corp.* would construct a 1,800-mile pipeline that would parallel the oil pipeline from the North Slope to Delta Junction, south of Fairbanks, then follow the Alcan Highway through the Yukon, British Columbia and Alberta, where it would connect with existing pipeline systems. Estimated cost: $7-billion.

Under provisions of the Alaska Natural Gas Transportation Act, cleared by Congress in October 1976, the President was directed to recommend by Sept. 1, 1977, which delivery system he preferred. Congress would have 60 days to act on the recommendation by joint resolution. If it disapproved, the President then would have 30 days to offer a second and final recommendation and Congress would have 30 days to approve or disapprove it.[23] Early in December 1976, the staff of the Federal

---

[21] "Man in the Arctic," *Mosaic* (magazine published by the National Science Foundation), May-June 1976, p. 3.

[22] Deposits that have been reasonably well identified and are rich enough to be worked profitably under current economic conditions. They are only a part of total resources, which include subeconomic, geologically predictable and speculative reserves.

[23] For details, see *Congressional Quarterly Weekly Report,* Oct. 16, 1976, p. 2995.

Power Commission recommended the Alaskan Arctic Gas proposal, calling it "vastly superior" to the other two on economic, environmental and engineering grounds. However, in November the Alaskan state government signed tentative agreements to sell large quantities of its "royalty" natural gas interests to El Paso, Tenneco and Southern Natural Gas Companies in an effort to win more support for El Paso's all-Alaskan pipeline proposal. Under the Alaska Natural Gas Transportation Act, the state was awarded one-eighth of the Prudhoe Bay gas—or about 3.3 trillion cubic feet—as its "royalty" share of the reserves.

A recent survey of Alaskan business leaders found that 85 per cent supported the El Paso proposal, while 12 per cent endorsed the Northwest Pipeline route and only 3 per cent preferred the Arctic Gas proposal.[24] On the other hand, environmental groups tend to prefer Northwest's Alcan route because it would follow existing pipeline or highway corridors. The stage thus appears set for a bruising battle in 1977, involving the White House, Congress and the state of Alaska, that could rival the oil pipeline battle in its intensity and import. Whatever route is chosen, natural gas probably would not begin flowing south until 1982 at the earliest.

Alaska also has enormous potential oil fields around its vast coastline. In 1971, the Federal Field Committee for Development Planning in Alaska estimated that "offshore potential in Alaska exceeds onshore." However, the panel cautioned, "Most of the offshore regions are located in areas of wild weather or heavy sea ice and will present substantial problems for safe production when oil is found." The only offshore production in Alaska thus far has been in Cook Inlet, southwest of Anchorage, where drilling for oil and natural gas has been under way since 1959 in areas leased by the state. The first federal sale of Alaskan oil and gas leases, in the Gulf of Alaska, was held in April 1976. Oil companies paid nearly $572-million for drilling rights on 81 tracts offered by the Interior Department in some 17,200 square miles of water off the state's southeast coast. The sale was the first of nine involving Alaskan offshore tracts that the federal government plans to hold by 1978.

Need to Develop Other Resources, Industries

The revenues Alaska receives from oil and natural gas development may help revitalize the state's other industries. After petroleum, fishing and timber are the second- and third-ranking sources of income. However, both industries have suf-

---

[24] The survey, known as the AftI-Dittman Poll, is conducted by the weekly business newsletter *Alaska from the Inside* (AftI), Dittman Research, Inc., and the monthly *Alaska Construction & Oil* magazine, where it appeared in the November 1976 issue, p. 10.

fered declines in recent years. Until the early 1960s, salmon fishing was the leading Alaskan industry. But it began to slump and the 1975 catch was only 26 million fish, down from 126 million in 1936. Logging also was strong until recently. The 1974-75 recession hurt lumber sales, and water-pollution regulations have threatened the closing of a major pulp mill in Ketchikan.

But in the November 1976 election, Alaskan voters approved a ballot measure to create an Alaskan Permanent Fund which will be fed by at least 25 per cent of all mineral royalties, bonuses and income from lease sales. The fund will be used, among other things, to modernize the fishing and timber industries. State officials also plan to encourage new industries to locate in Alaska. They envision cement plants to lower the costs of construction, and petrochemical or plastics plants to use some of the oil and gas supplies. Already, an oil refinery is being built near Ketchikan, another is being planned near Valdez, and a fertilizer company at Kenai is completing a $230-million expansion plan.

The state is investigating ways to tap economically its large reserves of iron ore, copper, zinc, tungsten, fluoride and gold. In addition, Alaska is believed to have at least one trillion tons of coal—enough to supply the nation for nearly two-thousand years at current consumption rates. But most of the known deposits are in such isolated and barren areas that mining and transportation would be extremely difficult. The state also plans to encourage its agricultural potential in an effort to reduce the high cost of food in Alaska. The Matanuska Valley northeast of Anchorage has fertile farmland and has produced grain, potatoes and record-sized vegetables despite a short growing season. Another area holding great potential for development is hydroelectric power derived from some of the state's great rivers.

But as development inevitably progresses in Alaska, it will become increasingly important to protect many of the state's natural and scenic areas from harm through human activity. Alaska still is the nation's last frontier, and the largest remaining wilderness. Its incomparable wildlife—caribou, grizzly bears, bald eagles, moose, walruses, polar bears and many more—must be allowed sufficient habitat to survive and prosper. Alaska's breathtaking scenery—mountains, forests, glaciers, lakes, sand dunes, ice floes, wildflowers—must not be permanently scarred. And the state's native population of Eskimos, Indians and Aleuts—some of whom still live as their ancestors did centuries ago by subsistence hunting—must be given the chance to determine their own future. These are perhaps the greatest challenges of Alaskan development.

Selected Bibliography

Books

Facts About Alaska—The Alaska Almanac, Alaska Northwest Publishing Co., 1976.

Gruening, Ernest, *The Battle for Alaska Statehood,* University of Alaska Press, 1967.

—*The State of Alaska,* Random House, 1954.

Keating, Bern, *Alaska,* National Geographic Society, 1971.

Peirce, Neal R., *The Pacific States of America,* W. E. Norton & Co., 1972.

Smith, Richard Austin, *The Frontier States—Alaska, Hawaii,* Time-Life Books, 1968.

Articles

Hodgson, Bryan, "The Pipeline: Alaska's Troubled Colossus," *National Geographic,* November 1976.

"How to Spend the Next Billion-Dollar Windfall," *U.S. News & World Report,* Aug. 2, 1976.

"Man in the Arctic," *Mosaic,* May-June 1976.

McPhee, John, "What They Were Hunting For" (two-part series), *The New Yorker,* Sept. 27 and Oct. 4, 1976.

Panitch, Mark, "Alaska's Pipeline Road: New Conflicts Loom," *Science,* July 4, 1975.

Rankin, Bob, "New Kinds of Obstacles Face Alaska Pipeline As Construction Nears End," *Congressional Quarterly Weekly Report,* Nov. 27, 1976.

Rau, Ron, "The Taming of Alaska," *National Wildlife,* October-November 1976.

Scheibla, Shirley, "Coming to a Boil—Competition to Carry Alaskan Gas Heats Up," *Barron's,* Sept. 6, 1976.

Schuyten, Peter J., "A Novel Corporation Takes Charge in Alaska's Wilderness," *Fortune,* October 1975.

Studies and Reports

Alaska state government, staff briefing paper, "A Preliminary Proposal Pertaining to National Interest ('D-2') Lands in Alaska Under the Alaska Native Claims Settlement Act," 1976.

—Department of Labor, "Economic Forecasts 1976-1978," 1976.

Alaskan Arctic Gas Pipeline Co., "New Gas for America," 1976.

Alyeska Pipeline Service Co., "Welding on the Trans-Alaska Pipeline," 1976.

Cooperative Extension Service, University of Alaska, "Alaska's National Interest Lands (D-2)—A Summary of Current Congressional Proposals," 1976.

Federal Energy Administration, National Energy Information Center, "Economic Impact of Oil Resource Development on the Alaskan Economy 1975-1985," April 1976.

Jones, Richard S., "Alaska Native Claims Settlement Act of 1971 (Public Law 92-203): History and Analysis," Congressional Research Service, Library of Congress, May 22, 1972.

Zemansky, G. M., "Environmental Non-Compliance and the Public Interest During Construction of the Trans-Alaska Pipeline," Fairbanks Environmental Center, September 1976.

ENVIRONMENTAL POLICY

by

John Hamer

1 9 7 4
Vol. II

ENVIRONMENTAL POLICY

F IVE YEARS AGO, on New Year's Day 1970, the National Environmental Policy Act (PL 91-190) was signed into law. It was a brief document, as federal laws go, only five pages long. But its purpose was broad: "To declare a national policy which will encourage productive and enjoyable harmony between man and his environment; to promote efforts which will prevent or eliminate damage to the environment and biosphere and stimulate the health and welfare of man; to enrich the understanding of the ecological systems and natural resources important to the nation; and to establish a Council on Environmental Quality."

President Nixon made the signing ceremony his first official act of the new decade, saying that "the 1970s absolutely must be the years when America pays its debt to the past by reclaiming the purity of its air, its waters, and our living environment. It is literally now or never." Nixon concluded his remarks by saying: "We are determined that the decade of the Seventies will be known as the time when this country regained a productive harmony between man and nature."

In the five years since the enactment of this law, commonly known as NEPA, it has proved to be perhaps the most powerful and far-reaching environmental legislation ever passed. It is considered the cornerstone of other environmental measures of the 1970s. Its strong provisions and their interpretation by the courts have forced federal agencies to incorporate environmental factors into the decision-making process. It has firmly established the concept of environmental impact assessment by requiring federal agencies to prepare statements explaining how proposed actions might affect the quality of the environment.

NEPA has given rise to an expanding body of environmental law, as citizen groups have gone to court to ensure governmental compliance with the act's provisions. Its approach has been adopted by more than 20 states that have enacted similar statutes and by a number of local governments. Furthermore, the act has had significant international repercussions. The environmental impact statement system has been embraced by

Canada and Australia, and has attracted considerable attention in several other countries.

The Council on Environmental Quality, in its annual report for 1974, concluded that "NEPA is alive and well. It has passed through a transition period, during which agencies have become aware of the act's widespread requirements, and the basic structure of the environmental impact statement process has been firmly established. NEPA has emerged as an integral and essential part of all federal agencies' activities. The foresight of Congress in passing NEPA has been widely recognized..."[1]

However, like many other fundamental departures in federal policy and procedure, NEPA has aroused controversy. It has been highly praised and bitterly condemned. Not long after its passage, it was called an "environmental bill of rights"[2] and potentially an "environmental Magna Charta."[3] Later, a writer said that "it has done more to preserve and protect the environment than all of the previous environmental protection measures combined."[4] Environmental lawyers sometimes refer to NEPA as "the great equalizer."

NEPA has been denounced by some government and industry officials as being too vague, ill-conceived and an opening wedge for harassment by environmental zealots. George F. Trowbridge, formerly an attorney with the Atomic Energy Commission, in 1970 spoke of the "atrocious piece of legislation...poorly thought out and ambiguous at all of the crucial points."[5] John A. Carver Jr., a former member of the Federal Power Commission, once called the act a "paper monster...of great potential harm."[6] During the legislative battle over the Alaska oil pipeline in 1972, the *Oil and Gas Journal* commented that life under the law has "approached chaos."

Richard A. Liroff, a political scientist on the staff of the Environmental Law Institute, wrote: "NEPA's vagueness has been in large measure responsible for both the statute's enormous impact and for the passions aroused in support of and in opposition to it."[7] Two other analysts declared: "In many respects, NEPA

[1] "Environmental Quality—the Fifth Annual Report of the Council on Environmental Quality," December 1974, p. 413.

[2] E. Hanks and J. Hanks, "An Environmental Bill of Rights: The Citizen Suit and the National Environmental Policy Act of 1969," *Rutgers Law Review*, Vol. 24, 1970, p. 230.

[3] R. Frederic Fisher, "Environmental Law," *Sierra Club Bulletin*, January 1971, p. 28.

[4] Peter Harnik, "Testing the Movement. It's Time to Save NEPA," *Environmental Action*, April 15, 1972, p. 3.

[5] Quoted by Hugh J. Yarrington, "The National Environmental Policy Act," *Environment Reporter*, Bureau of National Affairs, monograph No. 17, Jan. 4, 1974, p. 1.

[6] Quoted by Robert Gillette, "National Environmental Policy Act: Signs of Backlash Are Evident," *Science*, April 7, 1972, p. 30.

[7] Richard A. Liroff, "NEPA and its Aftermath: The Formation of a National Policy for the Environment," unpublished doctoral dissertation for Northwestern University, on file at the Environmental Law Institute, Washington, D.C.

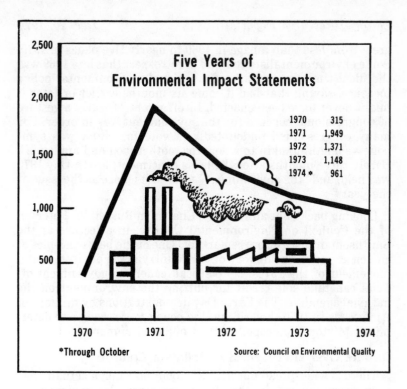

Five Years of Environmental Impact Statements

1970	315
1971	1,949
1972	1,371
1973	1,148
1974 *	961

*Through October   Source: Council on Environmental Quality

resembles a constitutional charter. It states a general policy in lofty terms, outlines a fragmentary procedure for implementing that policy, and leaves questions of detail to the good sense of those who must live with and interpret its requirements."[8]

Widening Public Acceptance of Ecology Movement

Passage of the act, it must be recalled, came at a time when the environmental movement was rapidly gaining momentum and "ecology" was fast becoming a household word. The Santa Barbara oil spill[9] had outraged the nation, Lake Erie was widely believed to be "dead," fires had broken out in Ohio's polluted Cuyahoga River, air pollution was getting worse in most major cities, open space was disappearing and park lands were threatened, endangered species lists were growing longer, and the real dangers of environmental degradation were beginning to dawn upon the American public.

The mass media were starting to sound the environmental alarm nationwide. The number of entries under "environment" and related environmental topics in the *Reader's Guide to Periodical Literature,* which indexes major magazine articles,

[8] Roger C. Cramton and Richard K. Berg, "On Leading a Horse to Water: NEPA and the Federal Bureaucracy," *Michigan Law Review*, Vol. 71, No. 8, January 1973, pp. 512-513.

[9] For background, see "Coastal Conservation," *E.R.R.*, 1970 Vol. I, pp. 141-160.

grew from less than a page in 1969 to nearly five pages in 1970. Some environmentalists contend in retrospect that late 1969 was the ideal time for passage of a national environmental policy measure, saying that had it come six months earlier or later it might never have been enacted. Liroff wrote: "Clearly a gesture of congressional concern for the environment was in order. For many congressmen, undoubtedly, a vote for NEPA was symbolic—something akin to a vote for motherhood and apple pie." Barely three months after the law's enactment, Earth Day 1970 was held, and "the environment" secured its place as the issue of the year.

Looking back on it all recently, Chairman Russell W. Peterson of the Council on Environmental Quality, in a lecture at the Smithsonian Institution, remarked: "One of the best examples of citizen action in the history of our country is the environmental movement of the 1970s. No political leader, no government official can take sole credit for putting the environment on the national agenda.... The Earth Day demonstrations by millions of Americans in 1970 showed that the people were ready and determined to stop the despoilment of our environment."

Dispute Over Effectiveness of Pollution Controls

There is widespread uncertainty about how much actually has been accomplished in the five years since the environment became a nationwide concern. While more people clearly are aware of environmental problems and many new laws aimed at environmental protection are on the books, concrete results in the form of decreased pollution and environmental improvement fall short of yesterday's high hopes. The evidence is decidedly mixed, and support can be found for arguments on both sides of the question.

"For a while, in 1969 and 1970, there was almost something called an 'ecology movement,' " Gene Marine wrote in *Ramparts* in December 1973. "It is gone, like a vagrant breeze across a meadow, leaving behind...a few traces, possibly important, possibly not." Marine argued that NEPA and the environmental movement were severely undermined by politicians and industrialists in the face of the energy crisis and economic difficulties. On the other hand, Judith Miller of *The Progressive* wrote at about the same time that "even some of the most ardent environmentalists concede that despite several setbacks caused by soaring prices, a sagging economy, and, most recently, the 'energy crisis,' the National Environmental Policy Act...has held up well..."[10] Miller cited several developments which "attest to the continued strength of the environmental movement."

[10] "Four-Year Score on the Environment," *The Progressive*, January 1974, p. 22.

One of the few measurable records of environmental progress is the National Wildlife Federation's annual environmental quality index, which tries to describe numerically the nation's environmental status in seven major categories: air, water, wildlife, timber, soil, minerals and living space. Thomas L. Kimball, executive director of the federation, has described the index as "a bold attempt to assign some values and form some judgments on those vital factors that make up the quality of our life—and to decide whether we were winning or losing the pollution battle."

"NEPA, overall, has resulted in a healthy reorientation of governmental perspectives and priorities."

James R. Schlesinger, then chairman
Atomic Energy Commission, March 1972

The group's fifth environmental quality index, released in early 1974, showed deterioration in every major category since 1970. "...The U.S. has spent more than $50 billion in the last five years, passed a host of anti-pollution laws and created an entirely new federal agency to enforce them," the organization said. "On balance, the results have been bitterly disappointing. In too many large cities the air is still not fit to breathe, and in too many parts of the country even the drinking water is contaminated. But perhaps most disconcerting of all, environmentalism itself has become an increasingly beleaguered movement."[11]

Nonetheless, there is substantial evidence that public support for the environmental movement remains strong. The Council on Environmental Quality in July 1974 released a compilation of public opinion polls and surveys taken by various federal agencies, members of Congress, and several public and private organizations. "The overall impression is that environmental issues remain very important in the minds of the public, especially as state and local issues," the council said. "The energy crisis and aftermath appears to have affected this relatively little."

Some of the most persuasive evidence of continuing support for environmental protection came in the November 1974 elec-

<hr>

[11] "Now the Real Battle Begins—The Fifth Environmental Quality Index," *National Wildlife*, February-March 1974, pp. 3-13.

tions. Candidates with strong environmental platforms were elected in numerous states, while many with questionable records on environmental issues went down to defeat. Environmental Action, a Washington, D.C., lobby group, compiles an election year "Dirty Dozen" list of 12 members of Congress who oppose environmental legislation. This year, eight of the 12 were defeated.[12] In addition, the League of Conservation Voters supports selected candidates with campaign contributions for pro-environment stands. Thirteen of the 17 candidates endorsed this year were victorious—including five out of six Republicans in an overwhelmingly Democratic election year.

Attacks Based on Economic and Energy Concerns

However, the environmental movement is likely to undergo increasing attack in the second half of the decade from those who see an inherent conflict between energy production and economic progress on the one hand and environmental improvement on the other. In this time of rising inflation, worsening recession and recurrent energy shortages, some politicians and business representatives already contend that environmental safeguards should be relaxed. President Ford has called for the preparation of "inflation impact statements" on all federally mandated rules and regulations. And some key industries complain that they are hard pressed to implement strict federal environmental standards.

The congressional Joint Economic Committee held three days of hearings in late November on the economic impact of federal environmental control regulations, and found spokesmen from the oil, chemical and utility industries united in favor of easing several standards.[13] On the other hand, spokesmen for federal energy and environmental agencies denied that pollution-control measures were contributing significantly to energy shortages or inflation and endorsed strong continued enforcement.

Assessing the economic impact of environmental programs is a tricky undertaking. For while the direct costs of pollution control equipment may be evident, the hidden costs of pollution itself are not always easily measured. Michael McCloskey, executive director of the Sierra Club, said recently: "Many of the so-called costs [of pollution controls] really represent merely a shift in who pays the costs. With controls, the producer of the pollution pays the cost, rather than the downwind breather who pays extra doctor bills to cope with emphysema; or the

---

[12] Glenn R. Davis (R Wis.), William H. Hudnut III (R Ind.), John E. Hunt (R N.J.), Earl F. Landgrebe (R Ind.), Robert B. Mathias (R Calif.), William J. Scherle (R Iowa), Frank A. Stubblefield (D Ky.), and Roger H. Zion (R Ind.). Winning re-election were: Samuel L. Devine (R Ohio), Dale Milford (D Texas), Sam Steiger (R Ariz.) and Burt L. Talcott (R Calif.).

[13] See *Congressional Quarterly Weekly Report*, Nov. 30, 1974, p. 3234.

downstream municipality that must pay extra to clean up a polluted water supply; or the downwind farmer or forest owner whose crops grow too slowly because of acid rainfall; or the factory worker who finds the paint job on his house ruined by factory fumes. The market costs of pollution are very real and somebody pays them."[14]

According to Environmental Protection Agency (EPA) Administrator Russell E. Train, a study done for the EPA by Chase Econometrics Associates forecast that pollution control programs would cause an average annual inflation rate of only about 0.3 per cent for the period 1973-1978 and a rate of only 0.2 per cent for 1973-1982. Train said other EPA research showed that sulfur oxide and particulate pollution caused measurable damages of $11.2 billion every year, compared with annual costs of less than half that amount to control the pollution.[15]

Train argued that environmental expenditures were neither a significant factor in the present inflation nor responsible for shortages of capital funds to any significant degree. He said all the available evidence showed that the benefits of pollution control far exceeded its costs. The Council on Environmental Quality released a study in November 1974 on "The Economic Impact of Environmental Programs" that further analyzed the trade-offs involved. It estimated cumulative pollution abatement costs over the 1973-1982 period at $194.8 billion, with $77 billion paid directly by the consumer (mobile air pollution sources and solid waste collection costs), $32 billion paid by the government and passed on to taxpayers, $32 billion paid by electric utilities and $54 billion by other industries—passed on to the consumer in the form of higher electric bills and product prices.

The council, like Train, said that pollution control expenditures had not been a significant contributor to inflation. According to the study, they accounted for only 0.5 per cent of the 17 per cent increase in the wholesale price index in 1973-1974. The study also found that:

> Projected investment for environmental purposes by U.S. industries would average only 3 per cent of total plant and equipment expenditures over the 1973-82 period, and would be unlikely to exceed 6 per cent in any one year.

> The impact of environmental expenditures on employment would probably be insignificant, with plant closings between January 1971 and June 1974 in part due to environmental regulations representing only 12,000 jobs, or .015 per cent of the current labor force.

---

[14] Quoted in the Sierra Club "National News Report," Nov. 27, 1974.
[15] Speech to the New York Chamber of Commerce and Industry, Oct. 3, 1974.

Environmental regulations would have no significant impact on foreign trade or the U.S. balance of payments.

Pollution-control programs would have some effect on the distribution of income. The average family which paid 0.5 per cent of its income for incremental pollution-control expenditures in 1972 (in the form of higher prices, tax revenues and government service charges) would pay about 2.0 per cent in 1976, and slightly less by 1980.

Despite such studies, many businessmen and industrialists remain skeptical that strict enforcement of environmental regulations is good for the country right now. They argue that pollution-control expenditures add little to productive capacity, drain resources from capital expansion that is needed to remedy shortages, and drive up consumer prices. *Business Week* magazine reported Sept. 14 that a survey by the economics department of McGraw-Hill Publications Company found business planning to invest $7.4 billion in air and water pollution controls during 1974. But total annual spending on new plant and equipment would be $112 billion, according to the Commerce Department.

National Policy Making and Enforcement

IN RETROSPECT, it is apparent that few members of Congress fully comprehended what they were creating when they passed the National Environmental Policy Act in late 1969. Nor did many other citizens realize what was happening, for the press and environmental groups took little notice of the congressional deliberations. In an extensive analysis of the legislative history of NEPA, Richard A. Liroff wrote: "Despite its broad implications, NEPA was not a highly controversial piece of legislation at the time of its consideration by Congress. Congressional consideration of NEPA was not marked by substantial in-depth media coverage. Nor were lobbyists for environmental and resource development interests to be seen busily visiting congressional offices and hearing rooms. NEPA was not even passed on a roll-call vote, and in this respect, its final passage stood in marked contrast to that of earlier more limited environmental legislation."

There was, however, protracted bargaining and considerable maneuvering as various House and Senate versions of the measure wound their way through the legislative process. In the Senate, there was a jurisdictional dispute between Henry M. Jackson (D Wash.), chairman of the Interior Committee who was NEPA's chief sponsor, and Edmund S. Muskie (D Maine), chairman of the Public Works Subcommittee on Air and Water Pollution. Liroff wrote: "At the heart of the disagreement between Senators Muskie and Jackson, two of the Senate's strongest advocates of environmental protection, was a fundamental difference over the conduct of environmental policy."

Jackson believed that NEPA would force "mission-oriented" public works agencies to consider environmental values early as they began to evaluate a project's environmental impact. But Muskie and the Public Works staff had doubts about the "self-enforcement" potential of NEPA's "action-forcing" provisions. They believed that some kind of outside policing mechanism was needed. The outcome was a compromise which included the key requirement that federal agencies prepare a detailed statement of the environmental impact of proposed actions, to be reviewed by other agencies.

"The most important job for environmental lawyers dealing with government agencies is to use all available means to persuade, embarrass, prod and force those agencies to do the job they should be doing anyway."

R. Frederic Fisher
Sierra Club

In the House, Rep. John D. Dingell (D Mich.), chairman of the Merchant Marine Subcommittee on Fisheries and Wildlife Conservation, was the chief sponsor of the bill. But Rep. Wayne N. Aspinall (D Colo., 1949-72), chairman of the Interior Committee, also worried about jurisdiction. He had misgivings about the measure's vagueness and tried to nullify its effect with an amendment providing that the act would not alter the responsibility or authority of any federal official or agency. Dingell was forced to agree to the amendment before the Rules Committee would release the measure for a vote in the House. The bill passed the House by a 372-15 vote—the only roll call in NEPA's legislative history—with the Aspinall amendment intact. But in the conference committee, where House and Senate versions of legislation are reconciled, Aspinall was outmaneuvered and the amendment deleted.

The conference, under Jackson's leadership, produced a report and a "statement of managers" which made it clear that all federal agencies had to comply fully with NEPA's provisions. Aspinall refused to sign the statement and argued against it on the House floor, but the House adopted the conference report by voice vote with little debate. The only other dissenter was Rep. William H. Harsha (R Ohio), who argued prophetically: "The impact of [the bill], if it becomes law, I am convinced, would be so wide sweeping as to involve every branch of the government, every committee of Congress, every agency, and every program of the nation."[16] The Senate also approved the conference report by voice vote, with virtually no opposition.

Reluctant Compliance by the Federal Agencies

Once the bill became law, it did not have an immediate effect on federal agencies. The Council on Environmental Quality's 1974 annual report explained: "Initially, the agencies were generally unaware of the requirements of the act. When the requirements were pointed out, most agencies adopted the position that NEPA did not apply to them at all—at least not to most of their programs—or, if it did apply, an impact statement could be prepared by their administrative staff as a finishing touch when the project went forward for final approval." The report added, that what began as a sharp departure from previous practice eventually became part of the federal decision-making process.

One of the complications during the initial period was that NEPA had no "grandfather clause" exempting projects that were already under way from compliance with the act, so federal agencies were forced to justify earlier decisions after the fact. Many of them deeply resented this and early compliance was often grudging and perfunctory. According to the Council on Environmental Quality analysis, this initial stage ended in April 1970 in the first major court decision bearing on the new law. In *Wilderness Society v. Hickel*, the U.S. District Court for the District of Columbia ruled that the Secretary of the Interior (Walter J. Hickel) could not grant permits for building a road through Alaska to be used in construction of the trans-Alaska oil pipeline until he had complied with the new requirement that an environmental impact statement be filed. "This decision gave reality and importance to NEPA," the council report said, and focused on the impact statement requirement.

For about the next three years there was a transition period in which agencies came to understand and follow the law's requirements. A number of basic questions arose during that time. What was meant by "major federal action significantly affecting the environment"? At what stage in the development of a project must an environmental impact statement be prepared? What

---

[16] *Congressional Record*, Dec. 22, 1969, pp. H 40927-40928.

must the impact statement contain? How could environmental consequences be predicted?

To help federal agencies answer these questions, the council began issuing a series of guidelines and memoranda. Under a presidential executive order (No. 11514) of March 5, 1970, it had been given primary responsibility for administering the system and reviewing individual statements. The council's initial "interim" guidelines, issued in April 1970, added key details to NEPA's legislative mandate. They required each agency to establish its own procedures for implementing the act, distinguished between "draft" and "final" impact statements, and stressed the early consideration of possible alternatives to proposed actions. One year later, the council issued revised guidelines which expanded agency review and emphasized public participation in the impact statement process. In May 1972, the council put forth further recommendations on what should be in the statements and how they should be prepared and circulated.

It was by no means a painless process. In an analysis of the first two years of NEPA, Robert Gillette of *Science* magazine wrote: "The law and its requirement of impact statements has forced, perhaps not obviously, nearly every agency—over 40 in all—to conduct a sometimes agonizing reappraisal of the way it performs its business and the way its business affects the environment. As a direct result of NEPA, the federal government this year [1972] will spend thousands of man-hours and perhaps $20 million that it never spent before to anticipate the adverse effects of pest-control programs, military installations, highways, and numerous other major and minor public works worth billions of dollars."[17] The third stage of NEPA development began with the promulgation of yet another set of revised guidelines in August 1973, establishing a comprehensive policy for the operation of the impact statement system.

Support for Environment in the Nation's Courts

Liroff of the Environmental Law Institute said that NEPA dictated "the direction, but not the magnitude" of a change in decision making, and because its guidance was not very specific federal agencies implemented it in varying degrees. "Environmentalists' raised expectations, their desire to see an elaboration upon NEPA's vague requirements, and their viewing NEPA as a last-ditch weapon to use against ongoing projects which they hitherto had unsuccessfully opposed—all combined to push many vital decisions about NEPA's meaning into the

---

[17] Robert Gillette, "National Environmental Policy Act: How Well Is It Working?" *Science*, April 14, 1972, p. 147.

Some Major NEPA Court Cases

Calvert Cliffs' Coordinating Committee v. AEC (1971). The U.S. Court of Appeals for the District of Columbia ruled that the Atomic Energy Commission's procedures for licensing a nuclear power plant in Maryland were unacceptable, that the AEC had made a "mockery" of NEPA, and that the commission had to determine for itself the impact of a nuclear plant's thermal pollution.

Environmental Defense Fund v. Corps of Engineers (1971). The Eighth Circuit U.S. Court of Appeals (St. Louis), ruling on the Army Corps of Engineers' environmental impact statement on the proposed Gillham Dam in Arkansas, expanded the importance of NEPA's first section.

Committee for Nuclear Responsibility v. Seaborg (1971). The U.S. Court of Appeals for the District of Columbia declared that the AEC's impact statement on its underground nuclear test on Amchitka Island in Alaska must set forth the full range of opposing views.

Kalur v. Resor (1971). The U.S. District Court for the District of Columbia ruled that the water quality permit program, established under the 1899 Refuse Act and administered by the Army Corps of Engineers, was subject to the impact statement system.

Natural Resources Defense Council v. Morton (1972). The U.S. District Court for the District of Columbia held that the Interior Department's environmental impact statement on its proposed sales of oil and gas leases on the outer continental shelf contained an inadequate discussion of alternatives.

Students Challenging Regulatory Agency Procedures (SCRAP) v. ICC (1973). This first NEPA case to be decided by the Supreme Court involved a challenge that Interstate Commerce Commission railroad freight rates discriminated against recyclable material. Although the Court upheld the ICC's rate increase, the decision broadened the rights of citizen groups to bring suit under NEPA.

Scientists' Institute for Public Information v. AEC (1973). U.S. District Court for the District of Columbia ruled that the AEC was required to prepare an environmental impact statement on the entire liquid metal fast breeder reactor (LMFBR) program rather than merely on individual power plants.

courts." It was indeed in the courts that NEPA proved to be a strong watchdog rather than a paper tiger. The nation's courts, for the most part, have interpreted the act's broad provisions literally and enforced its specific provisions stringently. Of the approximately 500 suits that have been filed under NEPA nationwide, federal district and appeals courts have handed down more than 200 decisions. The vast majority have strengthened the act and expanded its scope.

Frederick R. Anderson of the Environmental Law Institute, in the preface to his book *NEPA in the Courts* (1973), wrote: "As might be expected from so much litigation, NEPA fairly bristles with judicial glosses.... Failure to comply with NEPA usually carries a serious penalty: an injunction restraining the agency from further action pending strict compliance with the act. Routine implementation of NEPA through litigation may not be a very realistic or desirable prospect, but litigation does afford the courts both the opportunity to castigate misuse of discretion and to point the way toward adequate administrative oversight of the NEPA process."[18]

Some critics contend that NEPA is being interpreted too strictly by the courts, and that judges have given the act a potency which they say Congress never anticipated or intended. "The courts have been vigilant—perhaps even too vigilant—in implementing the NEPA requirements," Roger C. Cramton and Richard K. Berg wrote in the *Michigan Law Review*. Although agency resentment has subsided considerably, there still are many federal officials who consider it a weapon of harassment and delay in the arsenal of environmental activists.

Environmentalists are generally pleased with the way NEPA has evolved. Nonetheless, satisfaction with NEPA's operation is not universal among environmental lawyers. Gus Speth of the Natural Resources Defense Council said in an interview: "If anything, NEPA hasn't lived up to the expectations. It hasn't worked the way it should have. We've criticized too many impact statements to say that. It hasn't built an environmental conscience into federal agencies. They've tried to pass the buck to consultants and haven't done the hard thinking on the impact of their activities. It hasn't done the job because it hasn't reformed the agencies, but it has had a good educational effect and brought environmental concerns before the public."

Attempts in Congress to Weaken 1969 Legislation

If NEPA has not reformed the agencies, they have at least become intimately familiar with it. Nearly every federal agency has prepared environmental impact statements, and most agencies have been subject to NEPA lawsuits. Even the Central Intelligence Agency has procedures for complying with the act. Only two agencies—the Price Commission and the Pacific Islands Trust Territory Government—have been exempted from compliance with NEPA by the courts.

---

[18] Frederick R. Anderson, *NEPA in the Courts—A Legal Analysis of the National Environmental Policy Act* (1973), pp. ix-x.

Since it first became apparent that the law had teeth, it has been the target of uneasy legislators and lobbyists. For the most part, Congress has resisted recurrent efforts to weaken or bypass the act. In the book *Federal Environmental Law* (1974), Frederick R. Anderson of the Environmental Law Institute wrote that despite such attempts NEPA has fared well in Congress. Indeed, Congress has lifted the act's requirements in only four instances—the Alaskan oil pipeline, EPA's water-quality control program, the San Antonio North Expressway, and EPA's actions under the Clean Air Act of 1970.

"NEPA is becoming more secure. A frontal attack has no chance."

Frank Potter, staff member, House
Fisheries and Conservation Subcommittee

But during the first three years after the law's enactment hundreds of bills were introduced in Congress in behalf of various agencies and industries trying to avoid its mandate. The press reported that the act had created a backlash, and its opponents in Congress became outspokenly critical. Rep. Jim Wright (D Texas), a powerful member of the House Public Works Committee, said in April 1972 that he wanted to "short-stop all these pestiferous suits that are hamstringing the programs."[19]

The first exemption granted any agency was contained in the Federal Water Pollution Control Act Amendments of 1972, freeing the EPA from the impact statement requirements for all actions under the program except the issuance of discharge permits for new sources of pollution and the awarding of federal grants for public sewage treatment plants. The move highlighted a long debate over whether or not EPA was subject to NEPA's provisions at all. During Senate action on the water pollution bill, Senator Muskie said that EPA should be given a blanket exception, while Senator Jackson disagreed. The issue had been left unclear when Congress enacted the law in 1969. However, under congressional pressure, the EPA in October 1974 began to prepare impact statements on most of its major projects.

In June 1974, in a bill amending the 1970 Clear Air Act to save energy and encourage coal use, Congress exempted all EPA actions under the act from NEPA's environmental impact

[19] Quoted in *The New York Times*, April 30, 1972.

statement requirements. In the San Antonio expressway case, the statement requirements were circumvented rather than exempted. The Federal Aid Highway Act of 1973 terminated the expressway as a federal-aid project and allowed it to be completed with state funds. Thus it was no longer subject to the environmental act's requirements. The most significant exemption granted so far has been for the trans-Alaskan pipeline, but it was approved only after pipeline proponents took major steps to comply with the act. Even then the vote was extremely close, 50 to 49 in the Senate where Vice President Spiro T. Agnew cast the deciding vote. The House vote on the exemption was 221 to 198.

Future Implications of Environmental Law

THROUGH OCTOBER 1974, according to the Council on Environmental Quality, a total of 5,744 environmental impact statements were filed on federal actions, as required by NEPA. The Transportation Department filed the largest number over the past five years, followed by the Army Corps of Engineers, the Interior Department, the Atomic Energy Commission and the Federal Power Commission.

More agencies become involved every year, with the Federal Energy Administration, the Labor Department, and the Architect of the Capitol filing statements for the first time in recent months. In addition, U.S. District Court Judge Charles R. Richey ruled Dec. 12 that the Securities and Exchange Commission must draw up new regulations requiring the more than 11,-000 companies which it regulates to consider the environmental impact of their actions.

While many persons question the extent to which NEPA has truly changed the federal decision-making process, there is widespread agreement that it has had a salutary effect upon the bureaucracy. In their analysis, Roger C. Cramton and Richard K. Berg wrote: "In the short time since its enactment, the act has produced...a dramatic change in the perspectives of a number of federal agencies. Even more change...is around the corner." Cramton and Berg listed five major effects of the act:

> First, NEPA is an important step in a national reordering of priorities. For the first time, Congress has declared that federal agencies must consider environmental values along with other relevant factors in making decisions....

Second, NEPA requires an "airing" of the issues involved in governmental decision making. It opens formerly closed administrative procedures to public view and to public comment....

Third, NEPA forces agencies to articulate and to explain their decisions. Agencies must not only invite and listen to outside comments, but they must in practice respond....

Fourth, NEPA contains a built-in mechanism for leading the bureaucratic horses to environmental waters.... A great virtue of NEPA's requirements is that they build into the bureaucracy an instrument for orderly social change....

Finally, NEPA is not a toothless tiger that can be ignored whenever it suits the convenience of a federal agency. The citizen suit provides an extraordinarily flexible and effective enforcement technique, at least against administrative agencies.

Still, some argue that in many agencies compliance is more cosmetic than genuine—that bureaucrats have learned how to fulfill the act's minimal requirements without drawing criticism. "...Agency heads have come to recognize that a deftly written impact statement can make all the difference between smooth sailing for a program and complete paralysis," Gillette wrote in *Science* magazine. On the other hand, there is considerable evidence that some contemplated federal projects have been cancelled at an early stage because of obvious potential conflict with NEPA. Gary Widman, general counsel of the Council on Environmental Quality, said in an interview: "We get statements all the time that projects are cancelled. They never see the light of day, never get past the inner sanctum."

State Use of Environmental Impact Statements

Since 1970, according to the council, 21 states and Puerto Rico have adopted environmental impact-statement requirements similar to those in NEPA. Thirteen of the states and Puerto Rico have legislated comprehensive impact-statement laws: California, Connecticut, Hawaii, Indiana, Maryland, Massachusetts, Minnesota, Montana, North Carolina, South Dakota, Virginia, Washington and Wisconsin. Three states—Michigan, New Jersey and Texas—have administratively required impact statements. And five states require statements on certain projects: Arizona (water-oriented programs), Georgia (toll roads), Nevada (power-plant siting), Nebraska (state highways) and Delaware (coastal zone and wetlands projects). At least 15 other states are currently considering the adoption of impact-statement requirements, according to the council.

California has perhaps the most ambitious and far-reaching "little NEPA" law in the form of the California Environmental Quality Act. It has become a powerful tool for land-use control because of a California Supreme Court ruling in September 1972 that the law applied to private as well as public projects.[20] About 6,000 environmental impact statements are prepared every year in the state, according to the council report, compared with about 200 annually in Washington and between 10 and 50 per year in the other states with "little NEPAs." Finally, at least two municipalities—New York City and Bowie, Md.—have environmental impact statement requirements.

International Impact of Environmental Policy

Just as pollution by one country may have global effects, a national attempt to control pollution may have an international impact. U.S. laws aimed at preventing environmental degradation have been observed and imitated around the world, and NEPA is a notable example. "NEPA has had unique and important effects on the international community," the council report said. "That this domestic law should have such an impact testifies to its particularly broad administrative scope and to its conceptual strength."[21]

NEPA has had international impact in several ways. First, U.S. agencies such as the State Department and the National Science Foundation have applied NEPA to their activities abroad. Second, impact statements have been prepared by the United States for consideration in negotiating several international agreements, including the Ocean Dumping Convention, the Endangered Species Convention and the Oil Pollution Convention. Also, statements have been filed on U.S. projects that might affect neighboring nations, such as the salinity control project in the Colorado River, involving Mexico, and the Bureau of Reclamation's Garrison diversion project in North Dakota, affecting Canada.

But perhaps more important is the adoption of NEPA-like procedures by other countries. Australia requires an interim impact statement at the federal level, and the state of Tasmania established such a requirement in 1973. Canada imposed similar requirements in April 1974, and Israel recently directed its environmental protection service to draw up impact-statement procedures. The system has attracted considerable interest in West Germany and other European countries. However, there is deep concern about what effect, if any, environmental policy laws will have in underdeveloped countries, where the primary environmental problems are likely to be famine, disease and poverty.

---

[20] Friends of Mammoth v. Board of Supervisors of Mono County, in which a group of homeowners opposed construction of a high-rise apartment at Mammoth Mountain ski resort in the High Sierras. See "Restrictions on Urban Growth," *E.R.R.*, 1973 Vol. I, p. 85.
[21] See "Global Pollution," *E.R.R.*, 1971 Vol. II, p. 925.

Selected Bibliography

Books

Anderson, Frederick R., *NEPA in the Courts—A Legal Analysis of the National Environmental Policy Act*, Resources for the Future, Inc., 1973.

Dolgin, Erica L., and Thomas G.P. Guilbert (eds.), *Federal Environmental Law*, Environmental Law Institute, 1974.

Sax, Joseph L., *Defending the Environment*, Vintage Books, 1972.

Articles

Cramton, Roger C., and Richard K. Berg, "On Leading a Horse to Water: NEPA and the Federal Bureaucracy," *Michigan Law Review*, Vol. 71, No. 8, January 1973.

Fisher, R. Frederic, "Environmental Law," *Sierra Club Bulletin*, January 1971.

Fishman, Steven B., "A Preliminary Assessment of the National Environmental Policy Act of 1969," *Urban Law Annual*, 1973.

Gillette, Robert, "National Environmental Policy Act: How Well Is It Working?" *Science*, April 14, 1972.

Harnik, Peter, "Testing the Movement. It's Time to Save NEPA," *Environmental Action*, April 15, 1972.

Kreith, Frank, "Lack of Impact," *Environment*, January-February 1973.

Marine, Gene, "Scorecard on the Environment," *Ramparts*, December 1973.

Miller, Judith, "Four-Year Score on the Environment," *The Progressive*, January 1974.

"Now the Real Battle Begins—The Fifth Environmental Quality Index," *National Wildlife*, February-March 1974.

"The Surprisingly High Cost of a Safer Environment," *Business Week*, Sept. 14, 1974.

Yarrington, Hugh J., "The National Environmental Policy Act," *Environment Reporter*, Monograph No. 17, Jan. 4, 1974.

Studies and Reports

Council on Environmental Quality, "Environmental Quality—1974," fifth annual report and selected previous reports.

—"The Economic Impact of Environmental Programs," November 1974.

Fogarty, John, "Public Opinion and the Environment," memorandum for CEQ correspondents, July 31, 1974.

Liroff, Richard A., "NEPA and its Aftermath: The Formation of a National Policy for the Environment," unpublished doctoral dissertation for Northwestern University, on file at Environmental Law Institute, Washington, D.C.

U.S. House of Representatives, Subcommittee on Fisheries and Wildlife Conservation, "Administration of the National Environmental Policy Act—1972," hearings on Feb. 17, 25, May 24, 1972.

U.S. Senate, Committee on Public Works and Committee on Interior and Insular Affairs, "National Environmental Policy Act," joint hearings, March 1, 7, 8 and 9, 1972.

JOB HEALTH AND SAFETY

by

Helen B. Shaffer

Dec. 24
1 9 7 6

JOB HEALTH AND SAFETY

I F STATISTICS on job-connected injury, illness and death could tell the whole story, there would be rejoicing in the American workplace. The latest government figures, considered alone, would indicate that the problem was lessening *(see table, p. 192)*. Unfortunately, statistics do not tell the whole story. Concern for job safety actually has increased, and for good reason.

In addition to the usual kinds of injuries or fatalities caused by falls, fires and machinery, an ominous succession of new hazards have come to light in recent years and months. Toxic substances associated with work and either imperceptible to the worker or ignored by him have been taking a terrible toll, sometimes not until years after exposure. These newer forms of occupational hazards are the byproducts of technological advance and are far more difficult to overcome than the older and more obvious kinds.

The severity of much occupational illness, which may strike robust workers in their prime years, adds an element of tragic drama to the situation. In addition, each new revelation of a hitherto-unsuspected health hazard arouses fear that there may be other harmful substances, as yet undetected.

Another factor arousing public interest is that a dangerous condition in the workplace may menace the health of the population at large. The worker may bring the unseen contamination home, possibly in his clothing, and thus spread the infection to his family and others. Or the substance that he deals with in high concentration while at work may be found in a product that is widely distributed for use by the consumer. A familiar example is an agricultural pesticide that is capable of making farm workers ill and also contaminates crops sent to market.

The link between hazards of the workplace and the general environment was demonstrated Dec. 10 when chlorine gas leaked from a tank at an Allied Chemical Corp. plant and drifted in a poisonous cloud along the Mississippi River near Baton Rouge, La. Some 10,000 persons had to leave the area to escape the threat of poisoning.

191

Occupational Injury and Illness
in American Industry

Year	Total Cases	Rate Per 100 Workers	Number of Fatalities
1975	4,983,100	9.1	5,300
1974	5,915,800	10.4	5,900
1973	6,100,000	11.0	5,700
1972	5,700,000	10.9	5,500

Source: U.S. Bureau of Labor Statistics

Attention has also centered on occupational health because of controversy over a six-year-old government program to reduce those hazards. This program, authorized by Congress in 1970, vested enforcement responsibility in a new agency, the Occupational Health and Safety Administration (OSHA), in the Department of Labor. Never has an agency created for so benign a purpose been so persistently assailed by critics from so many sides.

Pressures for Revising Safety Provisions

Business, labor, consumer groups, politicians to the right and to the left, other government agencies, and even persons within the agency have had their say on what's wrong with the program. Critics include those who would strengthen the government's hand, those who would weaken it in favor of voluntary compliance, and those who would abolish the whole enterprise. Controversy has arisen particularly on standards of safety to be imposed on employers in regard to permissible concentrations of pollution in the workplace.

The controversy has generated many proposals for legislative reform—about 100 bills in every congressional session since OSHA was founded. Similar pressures for amending the law can be expected in the 95th Congress, which convenes Jan. 3, 1977. President-elect Carter has mentioned "safe working conditions" among his goals for the nation. A political campaign document from the Carter forces pointed out that, as governor of Georgia, Carter "took positive steps to improve working conditions and work-related health and safety programs" in his state. It added, "As President, he would continue this commitment and strengthen or extend existing OSHA legislation so that those who earn their living by personal labor can work in safe and healthy environments."[1]

---

[1] "Jimmy Carter on Labor," undated.

Organized labor and its friends often accused the Ford and Nixon administrations of helping the business community resist government regulation and especially the establishment of stringent (and costly) standards of environmental decontamination. Business interests, on the other hand, consider some of the regulatory standards unnecessary, unworkable, and arbitrary. Sen. Harrison A. Williams Jr. (D N.J.), author of the act creating OSHA and chairman of the Senate Labor and Public Welfare Committee which has kept a close watch on its activities, told a trucking industry conference[2] on Dec. 8 that he would continue to press the agency for more effective enforcement of the law.

Common Causes of Occupational Injuries

A cumulative listing of the multifarious hazards of the workplace would give so overwhelming an impression of danger that it might discourage all but the bravest to seek employment of any kind. But most of the hazards are familiar in all circumstances of modern life and the odds on being injured can be vastly reduced by taking ordinary precautions or reasonable safety measures. The most frequent causes of accidents on the job, cited in a recent comprehensive study of occupational health and safety,[3] are the following:

Fires and explosions from chemicals, pressurized containers or transmission lines.

Physical injury, possibly dismemberment, from unshielded parts of machines that saw, mold, roll, cut, mix, flatten, bend, grind, or simply move under mechanical power.

Electrical hazards from improper grounding or shielding.

Injuries to the eye from wood or metal chips discharged during cutting or grinding—or from the splashing or misting from liquid aerosols.

Crushing and mangling injuries from moving and lifting equipment, especially prevalent in construction and stevedoring.

Falls from equipment or from high places of work, most frequent in farming and construction work.

Mining has long been viewed as a particularly hazardous occupation because of the danger of underground accidents and the health-damaging effects of coal dust. Mining disasters make a particularly strong call on public sympathy and usually are followed by controversy over responsibility for the accident. Despite passage of the Coal Mine Health and Safety Act in 1969, according to a congressional report, mine accidents have

[2] Regular Common Carrier Conference, Orlando, Fla., Dec. 8, 1976.
[3] Nicholas Ashford, *Crisis in the Workplace: Occupational Disease and Injury, a Report to the Ford Foundation* (1976), pp. 69-70.

Occupational Injury and Illness by Industry

Type of Work	1974	1975	Type of Work	1974	1975
Contract construction	18.3	16.0	Wholesale and retail trade	8.4	7.3
Manufacturing	14.6	13.0	Services	5.8	5.4
Mining	10.2	11.0	Finance, insurance and real estate	2.4	2.2
Transportation and public utilities	10.5	9.4			
Agriculture, forestry and fisheries	9.9	8.5			

Source: U.S. Bureau of Labor Statistics

taken more than 1,000 lives and injured thousands more since that date.[4]

In the case of a mine or plant accident, the effect is instantaneous, the immediate cause not too hard to determine, and the extent of injury readily assessed. In the case of long-developing illness, it is difficult to determine the degree to which environmental pollutants contribute. Over the years, however, sufficient evidence has accumulated to implicate a number of substances in the workplace environment as factors in the incidence of serious disease.

The exact measure of the risk is beyond the powers of the experts; hence a variety of figures are bandied about. The National Institute of Occupational Safety and Health (NIOSH) has estimated that 390,000 new cases of occupational disease occur annually and cause possibly 100,000 deaths—far more than are counted by the U.S. Bureau of Labor Statistics *(see box, p. 192)*. Since its establishment in 1971, NIOSH has placed some 23,000 chemical compounds on its list of toxic substances that might, in sufficient concentration, be harmful to workers. But health research is time-consuming and cannot keep pace with the rate new chemical compounds are introduced in industry. Meanwhile, new and strange illnesses sometimes appear.

The worker's first symptoms may be so vague as to be dismissed—a pervasive or recurrent spell of fatigue, dizziness, shortness of breath, loss of appetite, difficulty in sleeping, visual or hearing irregularities. Since many of those afflicted are young, healthy men with little history of prior illness, there may be a tendency to postpone medical examination until the affliction is well-established. In some cases the damage is not

---

[4] House Committee on Education and Labor, Subcommittee on Labor Standards, "Scotia Coal Mine Disaster," a staff report, Oct. 15, 1976, p. 6. The report title referred to a mine disaster in Letcher County, Ky., in which two explosions, on March 9 and 11, 1976, took 26 lives.

revealed until some time after the individual has left the contaminated workplace. The damage may be irreversible.

Job-connected illnesses of this kind are by no means a new discovery. A British physician in the 18th century, Percival Potts, observed an unusual incidence of cancer of the scrotum among chimney sweeps, attributable to their overexposure to coal tar. Half a century ago, a number of young women who painted radium on watch dials became victims of cancer. Mme. Marie Curie, discoverer of radium, suffered radium burns and her death in 1936 was attributed to the cumulative effects of radium poisoning.

Illnesses From Dust, Gas and Chemicals

Among the best-known diseases associated with dust pollution are pneumoconiosis, the "black lung" of coal miners, and silicosis. Silicosis is prevalent among workers in mining, quarrying, stonecutting and glassmaking who inhale silica particles. It has been estimated that 200,000 coal miners or ex-miners suffer some degree of pneumoconiosis.[5] A study of 9,000 miners showed that the disease affected one-third of them to some degree and threatened more than 200 with disability or death.[6] According to OSHA, 1.1 million workers may be "at risk" from coal dust.[7]

Other well-recognized dust-origin diseases of the workplace are asbestosis, which afflicts miners and other handlers of asbestos; berylliosis, affecting workers in metallurgical, ceramic and other industries using beryllium; and byssinosis, sometimes called "brown lung," caused by breathing cotton dust. The "risk populations" for these conditions have been estimated at 350,-000 for asbestosis, 30,000 for berylliosis, and 800,000 for byssinosis.[8] Dr. Irving J. Selikoff, director of Environmental Sciences Laboratory of Mount Sinai School of Medicine in New York and a specialist in asbestosis research, has estimated that 400,000 of the 1 million Americans who work or have worked with asbestos will die of cancer during the next half-century unless far better treatment is devised.[9] He cited several studies that indicated the death rate from a rare form of liver cancer called mesothelioma was three or four times higher than normal among asbestos workers. In testimony before a Senate committee, Selikoff referred to asbestosis as a "hidden time

---

[5] National Academy of Engineering and the National Academy of Sciences, *Man, Materials and Environment*, a report for the National Commission on Materials Policy, March 1973, p. 75.

[6] "News from NIOSH," *Job Safety and Health* (an OSHA publication), January 1974, p. 33.

[7] Occupational Safety and Health Administration, "The Target Health Hazards" (1972), Bulletin No. 2051.

[8] Figures from public health sources cited by Nicholas Ashford, *op. cit.*, pp. 75-77.

[9] Statement at scientific conference at Cold Spring Harbor Laboratory, N.Y., Sept. 8, 1976.

bomb."[10] NIOSH said in August 1975 that garage workers who change or grind brake linings could be exposed to hazardous levels of airborne asbestos.

In matters of chemical toxicity, public attention tends to center on particular pollutants as cases of severe illness come to light. Vinyl chloride was in the news after the B. F. Goodrich Co. disclosed in 1974 that three workers in its Louisville plant had died of angiosarcoma, a rare form of lung cancer, apparently from breathing air contaminated with vinyl chloride—a colorless gas derived from chlorine and petrochemicals, and used in the manufacture of plastic products. The disclosure was followed by government efforts to impose stricter limits on permissible concentrations of the gas, and these efforts led to objections from industry that the limits were too strict. "The plastics industry has been shaken to its roots," *The Wall Street Journal* commented. The Louisville cases may constitute "only the tip of the iceberg."[11]

The next pesticide problem to capture attention involved workers at the Life Science Products Co. in Hopewell, Va. It was learned by early 1976 that 110 workers at the Hopewell plant had high levels of the pesticide Kepone in their blood. Twenty-eight were hospitalized with such symptoms as uncontrollable trembling and memory loss. All production of the pesticide ceased and the plant was razed. Allied Chemical Corp., for which Life Science was the sole supplier of Kepone, was fined $13.4-million in federal court for dumping the pesticide in the James River. Still the damage lingers on. Certain types of fishing have been banned in the James and the lower Chesapeake Bay, and civil suits by stricken workers are pending.

More recently, the spotlight has been on Leptophos, another pesticide, marketed as Phosvel. It was revealed that a number of employees and ex-employees of the Velsicol Chemical Corp. at Bayport, Texas, where the product is manufactured, showed symptoms indicating neurological damage. Leptophos has been manufactured in the United States since 1971 but for export only. It was implicated in the deaths of 1,200 water buffaloes in Egypt after the pesticide was applied liberally to crops in that country.

There appears to be no end to the succession of health hazards being reported to worker-protection authorities. Their concern is directed not only to contaminating substances but to such factors as excessive noise, heat, and vibration. A number of studies show that these conditions can contribute appreciably to

---

[10] Testimony before the Senate Commerce Subcommittee on Environment, Feb. 23, 1976.
[11] *The Wall Street Journal*, Oct. 2, 1974.

worker illness and debility. Excessive noise, according to one study, not only can impair hearing but "triggers changes in cardiovascular, endocrine, and neurological function."[12] A NIOSH official, commenting on the range of problems, said recently; "[W]e have been reacting in a crisis environment for the past two or three years."[13]

Development of Protective Laws

T HE NEED for government action to protect the health and safety of the worker became apparent as industrial activity expanded during the 19th century. The Massachusetts Department of Factory Inspection, established in 1867, was the first state agency to deal with job safety. Ten years later Massachusetts became the first state to enact a law imposing safety standards on industry; the standards applied only to the operation of spinning machinery in textile plants.

Other states followed with various types of job-safety laws. Though the protection was limited, the laws encouraged injured workers to bring damage suits against employers for negligence. This, in turn, encouraged support for proposals to establish an insurance system that would not only guarantee indemnity to an injured worker but relieve the employer of the expense of litigation and the risk of having to pay damages.

The principle of compulsory insurance was not readily accepted, however. Several early state laws to this effect were declared unconstitutional. Beginning with New Jersey in 1911, however, the states enacted workmen's compensation laws that stuck. Mississippi in 1948 became the last of the 48 states then in the Union to enact such a law.

A big argument for workmen's compensation was that it would encourage employers to maintain safe conditions in order to reduce their payment for casualty insurance. Studies over the years have not agreed on the effectiveness of the system in actually reducing work-connected injury and illness, although most studies have taken it for granted that the overall effect was beneficial. Some indicated that the accident rate dropped immediately after a compensation plan was adopted but the effect tended to level off as the years passed. Others attempted to show that the plans became increasingly effective as benefits were liberalized and worker-coverage extended.

---

[12] Nicholas Ashford, *op. cit.,* p. 75.
[13] Joseph K. Wagoner, director of field studies and clinical investigation for the National Institute of Occupational Safety and Health, quoted in the *Los Angeles Times,* June 27, 1976.

Congress, in the same act that created OSHA, ordered that a special commission be set up to look into "the fairness and adequacy" of workmen's compensation laws. Among the reasons for congressional concern, the act cited "the growth of the economy...increases in medical knowledge...[and] new technology creating new risks to health and safety." The presidentially appointed body, known as the National Commission on State Workmen's Compensation Laws, undertook an exhaustive review of the situation and issued a great deal of data and analytic material before it was disbanded July 31, 1972. It did note that accident rates were not necessarily lower in states where benefits were relatively high.

A more recent review, prepared by a research analyst on occupational health under a government grant, was even more skeptical of the supposed connection between high benefits and plant safety. While a study of available data showed the risk of serious work accidents had been appreciably reduced between the late 1920s and the early 1970s, it also showed the rate had declined for home accidents as well. Until definitive data become available to buttress their claims, he said, others should stop talking about "the beneficial effects of workmen's compensation on the occupational safety movement...."[14]

Spate of Protective Legislation in 1969-70

Until a very few years ago, the federal government was quite modest in its demands on private industry for the protection of employees. Nor was the issue of worker health and safety given prime attention by the public except briefly in the wake of a particularly sensational disaster. The Office of Industrial Hygiene and Sanitation had been established in the U.S. Public Health Service in 1914, but its work was (and remained over the years) mainly research and investigation. The agency had no enforcement duties.[15] Except for legislation pertaining to mines and railroads, the only direct intervention into private enterprise for worker safety was provided by the Walsh-Healey Act of 1936, which mandated health-safety standards for companies holding government contracts of more than $10,000.[16]

The situation changed during the 1960s. By this time the

---

[14] Lee Ellis, "Workmen's Compensation and Occupational Safety," *Journal of Occupational Medicine*, June 1976, p. 425. Ellis's research was financed jointly by the U.S. Bureau of Labor Statistics and the Kansas Department of Health and Environment.

[15] The agency underwent many changes of name and place over the years. In 1953, it became the Division of Industrial Hygiene within the newly created Department of Health, Education and Welfare. Later it became the Bureau of Occupational Safety and Health, and still later was transformed by the 1970 OSHA Act into the National Institute of Occupational Safety and Health. In 1973 the agency was transferred within HEW from the Health Services and Mental Health Administration to the Center of Disease Control in Atlanta, while still under the overall control of the U.S. Public Health Service—itself a branch of HEW.

[16] This protection was extended in 1965 to employees of suppliers of services to the government.

public had become sensitized to the issue of environmental pollution and there was general recognition that what harmed workers on the job could affect the well-being of the entire population. Meanwhile, in the 1950s, the number of reported industrial accidents had taken a sharp turn upward. This situation led to the enactment of the Coal Mine Health and Safety Act of 1969 and the Occupational Safety and Health Act of 1970. Still a third law, the Federal Railroad Safety Act of 1970, gave the Department of Transportation authority to regulate safety conditions on the railroads.

It has been said that federal laws concerning occupational health and safety now "cover virtually all of the nation's industry." And the three federal agencies chiefly involved—the Departments of Interior, Labor and Transportation—"have been given broad regulatory power and substantial appropriations with which to implement the federal law on health and safety."[17]

Coal Mine Safety; Black Lung Indemnity

Mine legislation has had a long history but one of limited protection. After a series of mining accidents, the U.S. Bureau of Mines was established in 1910 in the Department of the Interior. But the bureau did not acquire authority to inspect mines until 1941 or to set and enforce safety-health standards until 1952. A mine explosion in December 1951 that took 119 lives near West Frankfort, Ill., spurred enactment of the federal Coal Mine Safety Act of 1952. Under this law, the bureau could close a mine if conditions presented an immediate danger. But its authority extended only to mines that employed at least 15 persons, a restriction that was not lifted until 1966. In the same year, Congress passed the Metal and Non-metallic Mine Safety Act extending protection to other miners.

Another coal-mine accident, claiming 78 lives at Farmington, W.Va., on Nov. 20, 1968, spurred enactment of the most stringent of all mine safety laws, the Coal Mine Health and Safety Act. It became law on Dec. 30, 1969, establishing mandatory health and safety standards for underground mining—in contrast to surface, or strip-mining. The standards applied to fire protection, roof supports, escape ways, communications systems and permissible levels of dust.

In addition, the law required that miners be given chest X-rays when their employment began and periodically thereafter. If a miner was found to be developing black lung, he was to be given an opportunity to transfer to a job in a less dusty part of

---

[17] Frederick R. Blackwell, "Federal Safety Laws March On," *Natural Resources Lawyer,* fall 1974, p. 661. Blackwell is former chief counsel of the Senate Subcommittee on Labor.

the mine. The act also provided monthly cash payments to coal miners disabled by the disease or to their widows. Amendments to the act in 1972 liberalized these benefits to include all dependents in an afflicted miner's household as beneficiaries, extended coverage to surface as well as underground miners, and broadened the definition of black-lung disability.

Except for the black-lung-claims adjudication program, which is being transferred to the Department of Labor from HEW, enforcement of standards set by the act is in the hands of the Department of Interior. Interior in 1973 created a new agency, the Mining Enforcement and Safety Administration, to carry out enforcement duties.

The black-lung indemnity program has presented many difficulties. There were so many complaints about delays in processing claims that the House Appropriations Committee ordered a staff study of the problem. The study attributed the large backlog of cases mainly to shortages of personnel and to the complications of shifting the processing function from one department to another. "It might have been less an ordeal and less costly in the long run to have left the program with the Social Security Administration [in HEW]," the staff report concluded. But to reverse the decision now would only "create a more chaotic situation than now exists."[18]

New Principle Under 1970 Job Safety Act

The most significant development in the protection of worker health and safety was passage of the Occupational Health and Safety Act in 1970. It took effect April 28, 1971. The agency that administers the act has had several reorganizations and changes of leadership, and its activities have met with criticism and controversy. But the act did introduce something new into the governing principles of American life—that the worker has a legal right under federal law to a safe place to work. Moreover, the employer is now required, under penalty of law, to meet government-imposed standards of safety. This principle seems to have become firmly entrenched.

The act established in the Department of Labor a new agency, the Occupational Safety and Health Administration (OSHA), and created a new post of Assistant Secretary of Labor for Occupational Safety and Health to run it. In one way, the act represented a compromise between those who thought responsibility for worker safety should remain where it had traditionally been, with the states, and those who thought the time had come for the federal government to take a firm hand. The act provided that any state could develop its own occupational

---

[18] House Appropriations Committee, "Processing of Black Lung Benefit Claims," report by committee's Surveys and Investigations Staff, January 1976, pp. 7, 9.

health and safety program, but the plan and its operation would be subject to the federal agency's approval.

If a state plan is approved, the state may enforce it. But the federal office will evaluate the state effort for at least three years and may withdraw approval during that period. The act provided federal funding for 90 per cent of the cost of developing a state plan and for 50 per cent for the operation. To date, 22 states have had their plans approved, but only South Carolina has completed all steps and put its plan in effect.[19]

"The Congress declares...its purpose and policy...to assure so far as possible every working man and woman in the Nation safe and healthy working conditions..."

The Occupational Safety and Health Act
of 1970, Sec. (2) (b)

The act covers nearly all employees of companies in interstate commerce. Unlike many other regulatory functions of government, there are no exemptions by size of business.[20] The act applies even to employers of only one person, and "employee" includes everyone, including supervisors and corporation executives. Although the act applied originally only to civilian workers in private employment, executive orders from the White House extended the terms of the act to federal employees. Approximately 62 million people, 80 per cent of the nation's work force, are thus covered.

The law does not set standards but it empowers the Secretary of Labor to do so in specific situations, and it sets forth the procedures by which these standards are to be determined. The federal agency maintains a staff of inspectors who may enter a place of private business without notice to check on compliance. If a violation is found, a citation will be issued. If the citation is challenged, a hearing will be held before an administrative judge representing the Occupational Safety and Health Review Commission, another new agency established by the law.

---

[19] South Carolina's plan was certified on Aug. 3, 1976. The other 21 states are Alaska, Arizona, California, Colorado, Connecticut, Hawaii, Indiana, Iowa, Kentucky, Maryland, Michigan, Minnesota, Nevada, New Mexico, North Carolina, Oregon, Tennessee, Utah, Vermont, Washington and Wyoming.

[20] A rider on an appropriation bill in 1976 did exempt farms that employ fewer than 10 persons.

The judge's decision becomes final in 30 days unless sent for review to the full commission. Employers may appeal to the full commission or to federal court. Employees may appeal the proposed date for correcting a violation. Fines of up to $1,000 may be imposed for each violation and for each day of failure to correct the violation. Criminal penalties may be invoked if a death occurs from a willful violation.

The law also provides for research, training of personnel, and employee education on safety. The research function is a vital part of operations since standards on toxic substances are dependent on scientific findings. Responsibility for research is placed in the hands of the National Institute for Occupational Safety and Health, established by the act. The law orders the institute to develop "criteria dealing with toxic materials and harmful physical agents and substances which will describe exposure levels that are safe for various periods of employment, including...exposure levels at which no employee will suffer impaired health or functional capacities or diminished life expectancy as a result of his work experience." This standard-setting function has been the source of much controversy.

Problems in Safety Enforcement

CONFLICT is inherent in almost any worker protection program. While everyone applauds the goal of reducing the risk of worker injury, illness or death, there are large areas of doubt as to whether some of the safety measures—actual or proposed—are worth the cost involved. Inevitably, opinion differs on what action should or should not be taken.

All regulatory agencies of government inspire a certain amount of resentment among the people upon whom the regulations are imposed. Safety regulations touch an even more sensitive nerve than most. To the businessman, a citation for a violation is at best a nuisance. It is likely to be expensive and to offend him personally for implying that he may be heartlessly indifferent to the welfare of his employees. The small businessman, in particular, is likely to bristle at the sudden appearance of a government inspector armed with authority to look around his shop.

In a study of occupational health prepared for the Ford Foundation, Nicholas Ashford of the Massachusetts Institute of Technology observed that "inherent difficulties [are] encountered whenever the law is used as the predominant mechanism for social control of science and technology." He found this to be especially true of the OSHA program which "cannot be successfully implemented if we continue to ignore the fundamental conflicts and tensions which exist between various groups of people and between various institutions in our society."[21] Ashford described five sources of conflicts:

1. Self-interest, especially between management and labor which are accustomed to dealing with each other as adversaries.

2. Lack of sufficient data on which to base an unassailable decision—as in deciding how much abatement of contaminants in the air is required.

3. Differences in perception of "what is just or fair," for "honest men will differ and argue on how much control a government should exercise to protect its citizens."

4. Overlapping functions between government agencies, as in the case of OSHA and the Environmental Protection Agency.

5. Different parts of the total problem dealt with by "various professional interests." Unfortunately "the professionals, institutions and laws related to job health in our society have been historically quite separated from those related to job safety."

Complaints Against the Regulatory Agency

It is generally agreed, even within the federal agency itself, that OSHA made a clumsy start and was ill-equipped, both in funds and qualified personnel, to deal with the conflicts cited by Ashford. It is also generally agreed that the situation improved after Morton Corn, a University of Pittsburgh professor and specialist in industrial hygiene, took over as agency director a year ago.

President Nixon, on signing the OSHA bill, praised it as "one of the most important pieces of legislation...ever passed by the Congress." Nixon said it represented "the American system at its best: Democrats, Republicans, the House, the Senate, the White House, business, labor, all cooperating in a common goal—the saving of lives, the avoiding of injuries, making the place of work for 55 million Americans safer and more pleasant." His choice of OSHA administrator, George Guenther, however, was regarded as a political appointee lacking special qualifications needed to marshal united support from the diverse forces mentioned by Nixon.[22] Guenther's problem was compounded by a small budget[23] and an inadequately trained staff.

---

[21] Nicholas Ashford, *op. cit.*, p. 39.

[22] During the Watergate hearings, a confidential memo from Guenther, dated June 14, 1972, came to light in which he suggested using "the great potential of OSHA as a sales point for the fund-raising and general support by employers" and asked for suggestions "on how to promote the advantages of four more years of properly managed OSHA for use in the campaign."

[23] Some $35.7-million in the agency's first full year of operation, fiscal 1972; in the current fiscal year, 1977, it is $130-million.

One of the most pervasive complaints raised against the agency was that its inspection and enforcement staff concentrated on job safety as opposed to job health—that is, on physical conditions in the plant related to accident prevention rather than on concerns about worker illness. The factory and shop inspector traditionally was more attuned to accident prevention than to the more subtle hazards to health. Even worse were complaints that inspectors were issuing violation citations for minor technical deviations from standards—what became known as the "broken toilet seat violation."

Some of the difficulty arose from a provision in the act that required the agency to adopt immediately, as interim measures, appropriate standards already established by other agencies. The aim was to get the program started quickly while standards for newer hazardous situations were being developed. Accordingly, OSHA issued a number of so-called "consensus standards" to prevail for two years. These were drawn from existing standards, such as those established under the Walsh-Healey Act and by the National Fire Protection Association and American National Standards Institute.

Complaints followed that some of these standards were trivial, inapplicable or outdated. A kind of folklore grew up about absurd "violations" cited against places of business. In addition, businessmen and shop owners complained about the officiousness of inspectors. Richard P. O'Brecht, director of labor law for the U.S. Chamber of Commerce, told a congressional committee that criticism of the agency reflected not an absence of commitment to worker safety but the "frustration and often outrage caused by what many employers view as the heavy-handed application of the OSHA program."[24]

Federal Efforts to Correct Shortcomings

Small businessmen in particular were in distress. Rules and regulations were often so wordy and technical that proprietors had difficulty understanding them. "How can he [the employer] determine whether his wooden ladders are properly constructed and in compliance by being referred to 11 pages of fine print on the subject which includes everything from algebraic equations to the fibre stress characteristics of more than 50 different types of wood?" O'Brecht asked.

The small businessman has no one to turn to. Unlike the big corporation, he has no technical specialists to handle such problems. If he asks the agency to send an inspector to see if he is in conformity and to advise him on correcting any deviations from the standard, he stands in jeopardy of being cited for a

---

[24] Testimony before the Subcommittee on Labor, Senate Committee on Labor and Public Welfare, April 12, 1976.

violation. The Chamber of Commerce has long demanded a system that would permit on-site consultations with OSHA experts who would inform the proprietor if anything is wrong and advise him how to correct it—and give him a chance to correct it before citing him for a violation.

The agency has been trying to meet these criticisms. It has instituted a training program in "human relations" for its inspectors to help them deal more sympathetically with the small businessman. And it has written and rewritten manuals to offer compliance instructions in simpler language. Perhaps even more important, an effort is being made to enlarge the staff on health protection, as distinct from safety protections.

Recognizing that there is a shortage of qualified occupational-health inspectors and very few places where such training can be acquired, OSHA set up its own work-study program to attract potentially well-qualified individuals to fill the needed jobs. The goal is to obtain a corps of 2,200 specialists—1,100 safety inspectors and 1,100 industrial hygienists whose concern is primarily with the illness factor. Each group of specialists will be made aware of the problems of the other so that, for example, if a safety inspector suspects the presence of an airborne health hazard, he will call on an industrial hygienist to check it.

These measures have not allayed all criticisms. They have tended to deepen suspicion among labor unions that the agency is too ready to make concessions to business at the expense of worker health. Units of the Ralph Nader consumer-interest organization in Washington, D.C., keep up a steady flow of pamphlets berating OSHA—saying that it is not fulfilling its mandate or is going soft on industry.

Organized labor has its own list of recommendations for reform and these do not conform with those of the business community. The AFL-CIO has drawn up a list of proposed reforms. "It is time the federal government lived up to the promise...of a safe and healthy workplace for every American worker," the statement said.[25] Among the "specific actions [that] must be taken":

> More money for the agency, more qualified manpower and more facilities, including a laboratory.
>
> "Full federal preemption of promulgation and enforcement of occupational safety and health standards in all states."
>
> Coverage for all workers, including state and local government employees.

---

[25] American Federation of Labor and Congress of Industrial Organizations, "Policy Resolutions," adopted October 1975.

Authority to compliance officers to issue on-the-spot orders that employees leave places of "imminent danger."

Transfer NIOSH, the occupational health research agency, from HEW to the Department of Labor and also transfer health and safety responsibility for miners and railroad workers to Labor.

To these criticisms have been added others from the General Accounting Office, an arm of Congress, in a series of reports. The GAO noted that OSHA permitted states, while developing their programs, to maintain lower safety standards than are required by the federal government. Federal agencies themselves have been criticized in these reports as having inadequate worker-protection programs. The House Government Operations Committee, after several days of hearings, issued a critical report on Sept. 27, 1976, saying: "In its five years of operation, the OSH administration has failed to provide adequate protection for the health of American workers." But the committee was "encouraged" by the commitment for improving the program that was shown by the agency's director, Morton Corn.

Cost-Benefit Issue; Dollars Versus Risks

Behind all the arguments on worker health and safety lies the basic question of cost. It has become customary to apply the concept of a cost-benefit ratio to questions of policy in this area. To some it seems crass to balance a dollar figure against the health or life of a human being. It helps to consider the balance as between cost and risk, a more acceptable frame of reference, familiar to all in the form of insurance.

Dr. Philip Handler, president of the National Academy of Sciences, told a scientific forum: "There is no escape from the need, somehow, to equate dollars and lives, to agree to the dollar value of an average human life in the population at risk...."[26] In a later extension of remarks on this subject, Handler said: "[W]hen the government contemplates regulatory activity to diminish the risk associated with some technology...an attempt is required to state both the cost and the benefits in quantitative form."[27]

Generally speaking, the employer is more interested in the cost of instituting a safety or health-protection measure and the employee is more interested in getting the maximum amount of protection. It has been pointed out, however, that if the risk is not too great, the worker may prefer to forgo a safety measure in

---

[26] Talk at a National Academy of Sciences forum, "How Safe is Safe," May 1973, reprinted in Harold P. Green's "The Risk-Benefit Calculus in Safety Determinations," *George Washington Law Review*, March 1975, p. 798.

[27] Philip Handler, "A Rebuttal: The Need for a Sufficient Scientific Base for Government Regulation," *George Washington Law Review*, March 1975, pp. 809-811.

favor of some other benefit—higher wages, for example. Some studies are critical of unions that for years pressed for other benefits as alternatives to health-protective measures.

An academic critic of OSHA complained: "[T]he basic problem with the implementation of the act is that there is no fundamental agreement on the practical methods of balancing considerations of greater safety and health against considerations of cost." He argued that "the government...should not force more safety and health on society than workers would choose for themselves if they had to pay the costs...directly." "In their private lives," he added, "...they smoke cigarettes, drive when they could walk, ski when they could read a book, and use power mowers when safer hand mowers would do."[28]

That the cost of protection will be high is generally taken for granted. Nevertheless a government program of the OSHA type appears to have become a permanent element in the nation's economic life. And some of the early suspicion of the motives of the new agency administering the program has subsided. A spokesman for the construction industry has said that "most of our original apprehension has proven groundless." He said the agency "is neither as effective as some of its advocates thought it would be nor is it the obstacle to normal operations that was originally anticipated by industry." Of one thing he was sure: "OSHA is here and working and...it is never going to go away."[29]

---

[28] Robert Stewart Smith, *The Occupational Safety and Health Act* (1976), pp. 1, 34. Smith is an assistant professor at the New York State School of Industrial and Labor Relations at Cornell University.

[29] John A. Woodhall Jr., "After Five Years an Assessment of OSHA," *Construction*, April 1976, p. 29. Woodhall is chairman of the Central States Construction Division of Central-Allied Enterprises Inc., and chairman of the National Safety and Health Committee of the Associated General Contractors of America.

Selected Bibliography

Books

Ashford, Nicholas, *Crisis in the Workplace: Occupational Health and Safety,* MIT Press, 1976.

Brodeur, Paul, *Expendable Americans,* Viking, 1974.

Page, J. A. and Mary-Win O'Brien, *Bitter Wages: The Report on Disease and Injury on the Job,* Grossman, 1973.

Smith, Robert Stewart, *The Occupational Safety and Health Act,* American Enterprise Institute for Public Policy Research, 1976.

Articles

Blackwell, "Federal Safety Laws March On," *Natural Resources Lawyer,* fall 1974.

Chelius, James R., "The Control of Industrial Accidents: Economic Theory and Empirical Evidence," *Law and Contemporary Problems,* summer-autumn 1974.

Conn, Harry, "Quieting Ear Pollution," *The American Federationist,* October 1975.

Ellis, Lee, "Workmen's Compensation and Occupational Safety: A Review and Evaluation of Current Knowledge," *Journal of Occupational Medicine,* June 1976.

Ettkin, Lawrence P. and J. Brad Chapman, "Is OSHA Effective in Reducing Industrial Injuries?" *Labor Law Journal,* April 1975.

Klein, Edward A., "Warning: The Workplace May be Hazardous to Your Health," *Journal of Occupational Medicine,* June 1976.

Job Safety and Health, selected issues.

Page, Joseph A. and Peter N. Munsing, "Occupational Health and the Federal Government: The Wages Are Still Bitter," *Law and Contemporary Problems,* summer-autumn 1974.

Woodhall, John A. Jr., "After Five Years: An Assessment of OSHA, *Construction,* April 1976.

"Why Nobody Wants to Listen to OSHA," *Business Week,* June 14, 1976, p. 64.

Studies and Reports

Department of Labor and Social Security Administration, "Processing of Black Lung Benefit Claims," report to House Committee on Appropriations, January 1976.

General Accounting Office, "Better Data on Severity and Causes of Worker Safety and Health Problems Should Be Obtained from Workplaces," Aug. 12, 1976.

U.S. Congress, House Appropriations Subcommittee on Labor, testimony of Morton Corn, 1976, pp. 534-631.

U.S. Congress, House Committee on Education and Labor, "Scotia Coal Mine Disaster," a staff report, Oct. 15, 1976.

INDEX

A

Abbot, Charles Greeley - 12
Aerosols
  Alternatives - 62, 63
  Fluorocarbon debate - 53-55
  Typical products (box) - 54
Air Pollution
  Auto emissions - 99, 100
  Catalytic converters - 100
  Legislation - 98-101
  Nondegradation - 101
  Stationary sources - 100
  Urban compliance - 100, 101
Alaska
  Alaskan facts and figures (box) - 160
  Alaskan historic highlights (box) - 158
  Crime in Alaska (box) - 155
  Fishing resources - 167
  Mining resources - 167
  National interest lands - 156
  Native land claims issue - 154-156, 162-164
  Natural gas pipeline - 165, 166
  Offshore oil leasing - 166
  Oil pipeline - 147-152
  Oil royalties - 152
  Russian settlers - 158
  Social impact of construction - 153, 154
  Statehood question - 161, 162
  Timber resources - 167
  Where will Alaska's oil go? (box) - 151
American Indians
  National interest lands - 156
  Native land claims - 154-156, 162-164
  Water rights - 134, 135
Aspinall, Wayne N.
  Environmental policy - 179
Atomic Waste
  Fission products and byproducts - 26
  Hanford Reservation - 24, 32-35
  (See also) Nuclear Waste Disposal.

B

Bethe, H. A.
  Permanent storage of wastes - 23, 30
Bioconversion - 8
Brooks, Harvey
  Radiation risks - 27

C

California
  Coastal zone management - 70, 79
  Nuclear safety legislation - 28
Cancer
  Ozone link - 52

Carter, Jimmy
  Environmental protection - 83
  Nuclear waste disposal - 23
  Occupational safety - 192
  Waste recycling - 41
Church, Frank
  Clearcutting - 120
  Nuclear waste disposal - 35
Coastal Zone Management
  California program - 70
  Coastal Zone Management Act of 1972 - 67
  Delaware program - 70, 71
  Funding (box) - 69
  Legislation - 78-80
  Offshore drilling - 78, 79
  Public access to beaches (box) - 82
  Shoreline jurisdiction - 75-77
  Shoreline management costs vs. benefits - 83
  State coastal protection plans - 68-71
  State land-use regulations - 81
  States and coastal zone management (box) - 70
  Wetlands preservation - 76, 77, 83
Colorado River
  Central Arizona project (box) - 141
  Chronology of the Colorado (box) - 139
  Colorado River system (box) - 137
  Energy resources - 134
  Federal water diversion projects - 138
  International complications - 131
  Reservoirs - 132
  Rivers of the West (box) - 133
  Salinity levels - 131
  Water rights of American Indians - 135
Connally, John B.
  Offshore drilling - 78

D

Delaware
  Coastal zone management program - 70, 72
Dingell, John D.
  Alaskan national interest lands - 157
  Environmental policy - 179

E

Eisenhower, Dwight D.
  Alaskan statehood question - 162
Electricity
  Photovoltaic cells - 7
  Solar thermal conversion - 9
Energy. See Oil; Solar Energy.

209

INDEX

Energy Research and Development Administration
Interim surface storage of waste - 36
Permanent waste storage - 29-31
Plutonium reprocessing - 39-41
Radiation risks - 27
Solar energy projects - 14, 15
Spent fuel assemblies - 42-44
Willrich report - 28
Environment
Cleanup costs - 88-90
Council on Environmental Quality - 171, 172
Ecology movement - 173
Economic impact of environmental programs - 176-178
Environmental impact statements (box) - 173
Growth of environmental industry - 92, 93
International impact of U.S. policy - 187
1960s' movement - 77
Pollution and the public (box) - 89
Shoreline erosion - 72
Major NEPA court cases (box) - 182
State use of environmental impact statements - 186
(See also) National Environmental Policy Act.
Environmental Protection Agency
Kepone pollution (box) - 74
Low-level waste burial sites - 37, 38
Water and shoreline pollution - 73-75
Ericcson, John - 11

F

Fannin, Paul J.
Solar legislation - 14
Fluorocarbons
Industrial use - 48
Link to ozone depletion - 56-58
Production (box) - 49
Research efforts - 56-59
Restriction efforts - 62
Threat to ozone - 49-52
Ford, Gerald R.
Air pollution - 100
Coastal Energy Impact Act - 68
Environmental policy - 176
Waste recycling - 41
Western energy development - 134
Forest Policy
Clearcutting - 109-111, 119
Forest land in the U.S. (box) - 109
Legislation - 109, 112, 115, 117-120
Monongahela decision - 109-111, 119
Multiple use management - 123
National forest system - 116, 117
Postwar demands for lumber - 118
Renewable resource assessment - 113, 114

Southern Appalachian Multiple Use Council - 111
Timber harvesting methods (box) - 121
Timber reserves - 114-116
Timber tax policy - 117
Tree farms - 117

G

Goddard, Robert - 12

H

Harsha, William H.
Environmental policy - 180
Hatfield, Mark O.
Federal forest legislation - 112
Forest policy - 122
Humphrey, Hubert H.
Federal forest legislation - 112, 113

I

Indians. See American Indians.

J

Jackson, Henry M.
Alaskan national interest lands - 157
Environmental policy - 178, 179, 184

K

Kansas
Salt mine experiment - 35
Kennedy, Edward M.
Nantucket Sound Islands Trust bill - 82
Kepone Pollution (box) - 74

L

Lavoisier, Antoine - 11

M

Monongahela National Forest
Clearcutting ban - 109-111, 119

210

INDEX

54843

DATE DUE

GAYLORD			PRINTED IN U.S.A.